Homosexuality
and Pseudohomosexuality

HOMOSEXUALITY

AND

PSEUDOHOMOSEXUALITY

LIONEL OVESEY, M.D.
Clinical Professor of Psychiatry
Psychoanalytic Clinic for Training and Research
Department of Psychiatry
College of Physicians and Surgeons
Columbia University

SCIENCE HOUSE   NEW YORK

Contents

6 HOMOSEXUALITY AND PSEUDOHOMOSEXUALITY

Introduction Motivational Basis of Homosexual and Pseudohomosexual Behavior Theory of Therapy Prognosis Selection of Patients Special Problems in Therapeutic Technique

The author and the publisher wish to thank the following for granting permission to include materials published by them:

Chapter 1, "The Homosexual Conflict: An Adaptational Analysis," was first published in *Psychiatry: Journal for the Study of Interpersonal Processes*, 17:3, pp. 243–250, copyright 1954.

Chapter 2, "The Pseudohomosexual Anxiety," was first published in *Psychiatry: Journal for the Study of Interpersonal Processes*, 18:1, pp.17–25, copyright 1955.

Chapter 3, "Pseudohomosexuality, the Paranoid Mechanism, and Paranoia: An Adaptational Revision of a Classical Freudian Theory," was first published in *Psychiatry: Journal for the Study of Interpersonal Processes*, 18:2, pp.163–173, copyright 1955.

Chapter 4, "Masculine Aspirations in Women: An Adaptational Analysis," was first published in *Psychiatry: Journal for the Study of Interpersonal Processes*, 19:4, pp. 341–351, copyright 1956.

Chapter 5, "Psychotherapy of Male Homosexuality: Psychodynamic Formulation, Prognosis, Selection of Patients, Techniques," combines elements of two papers. The sections on the motivational Basis of Homosexual and Pseudohomosexual Behavior and on the Theory of Therapy appeared in "Psychotherapy of Male Homosexuality: Psychodynamic Formulation," co-authored with Willard Gaylin and Herbert Hendin, first published in *Archives of General Psychiatry*, 9, pp. 19–31, copyright 1963 by the American Medical Association. The sections on Prognosis, Selection of Patients, and Special Problems in Therapeutic Technique appeared in "Psychotherapy of Male Homosexuality: Prognosis, Selection of Patients, Technique," co-authored with Willard Gaylin, first published in the *American Journal of Psychotherapy*, 19:3, pp. 385–396, copyright 1965.

Chapter 6, "Case Studies of Male Homosexuality," appeared in "Psychotherapy of Male Homosexuality: Psychodynamic Formulation," co-authored with Willard Gaylin and Herbert Hendin, first published in *Archives of General Psychiatry*, 9, pp. 19–31, copyright 1963 by the American Medical Association.

Preface

THE papers in this volume were written over a ten year period, and the ideas expressed in them follow a logical progression. They originated from my dissatisfaction with the Freudian explanation for so-called "homosexual anxieties" in heterosexual males. I observed, as had Freud initially, and after him, many others, that heterosexual male patients, in the course of psychoanalytic therapies, frequently expressed wishes to be loved by men, to be dependent on them, to dominate or be dominated by them, and to establish physical—especially genital—contact with them. Inevitably, in the wake of such fantasies, the patient became afraid that he was a homosexual, and, in accordance with Freudian theory, the analyst had no choice but to confirm his fear. Freud attributed the fantasies to a feminine component in an inherited bisexual constitutional striving for gratification through a homosexual instinct. He, therefore, lumped them all together under the single heading of "latent homosexuality." The patient was then asked to come to terms with his "homosexuality" on the grounds that it was constitutional and hence not alterable.

In clinical practice, this explanation had a serious flaw, which was not easily surmounted; namely, the fantasies were unaccompanied by erotic feeling, except in those few heterosexuals, who were either overtly bisexual or suffered from true latent homosexuality. In all the others,

who comprised the great majority of heterosexuals, homosexual arousal or behavior, at least in adulthood, was con-
sistently denied, nor could I demonstrate its occurrence
clinically. It was common practice for many analysts under
these circumstances, so great was the influence of Freud,
to fall back upon theoretical preconceptions. In other
words, the theory was not challenged; it was simply assumed the patient was wrong. The analyst, therefore, insisted the feeling was repressed and accused the patient
of resistance to the analytic process. The patient, in turn,
objected that he was unaware of any homosexuality, but
this was easily countered by asking why he chose to deny
it. It was not an equal battle, since on issues of this kind,
insusceptible of proof, the analyst always had the upper
hand. In the end, most patients dutifully took the analyst's
word for it—intellectually, that is—and the analysis moved
on to more fruitful endeavors. The admission of homosexuality was then cited with circular reasoning as proof
of its existence. The fact is, of course, it proved no such
thing. The absence of clinical documentation made the
analyst's position completely untenable, methodologically
as well as operationally.

I decided, therefore, to discard Freud's instinctual explanation altogether and to reexamine the fantasies purely
from an adaptational point of view. I hoped by changing
the frame of reference I could perhaps discern an adaptive
purpose to the fantasies other than the homosexual one
postulated by Freud. I began to pay attention to the motivational context in which the fear of being homosexual
became manifest in heterosexual males. I asked myself
the following question: What are the unconscious motivations that impel a heterosexual male in his fantasies to
seek contact with another man's genitals? I found in every
instance where there was no evidence of homosexual

arousal, the fantasies were motivated either by dependency needs or by power needs. Why, then, did the patient misperceive them as homosexual? The trouble lay in their content; that is, in the imagery. The patient attempted in the fantasies to achieve dependency and power goals through the symbolic use of the genital organs for non-sexual purposes. In consequence, he misinterpreted the images in his fantasies as truly homosexual. In reality, however, they were only symbolically homosexual, or, as I labeled them, pseudohomosexual, and the related anxiety, therefore, was a pseudohomosexual anxiety.

I had by this time concurrently become involved in a research investigation of the treatability of male homosexuality. Here, again, I was challenged by the Freudian doctrine, which held that homosexuality was a fixed, genetic entity that could not be treated. I saw the disorder, however, in adaptational terms as a neurotic symptom with a developmental history, and I felt, as such, it should be responsive to psychotherapy. I assessed the behavior of my homosexual patients adaptationally and broke it down into its motivational components. It soon became clear that the homosexual act was not governed by the wish for homosexual gratification alone; but also by two nonsexual motivations of dependency and power. These two motives played the same symbolic roles for the homosexual that they played in the nonerotic, pseudohomosexual fantasies of the heterosexual male. They influenced not only the physical mechanics of the homosexual act, but were important determinants in the psychosocial structure of the homosexual relationship. There was, of course, a vital difference between the heterosexual male and the homosexual male in the way they handled the nonsexual motivations. The heterosexual male satisfied his dependency and power needs only in fantasy, and, as a result, developed a pseudohomosexual anxiety; the homosexual male, on the other hand, acted them out in the overt homosexual act at the same time that he satisfied himself sexually. Any anxiety he had about being homosexual, therefore, was a true homosexual anxiety.

The first paper, "The Homosexual Conflict," provides the theoretical framework for all the others. In it, after a review of Freud's theory of homosexuality, I recast the psychodynamics of male homosexuality in an adaptational context, formulate the concept of pseudohomosexuality, and draw upon case examples to document the clinical basis of my formulations. The second paper, "The Pseudohomosexual Anxiety," is an elaboration of the pseudohomosexual hypothesis. It consists of a case study designed to accomplish two things: first, to demonstrate the psychodynamics of pseudohomosexuality as they emerge in the treatment of a typical patient; and second, to demonstrate the practical application of these psychodynamics in the conduct of psychotherapy. The third paper, "Pseudohomosexuality, the Paranoid Mechanism, and Paranoia," is an adaptational revision of a classical Freudian theory. Freud proposed that repressed homosexuality was the hidden cause of paranoia. I make use of the concept of pseudohomosexuality, however, to demonstrate that paranoia can stem from nonsexual adaptations to societal stimuli, and motivationally need have nothing to do with homosexuality whatsoever. The fourth paper, "Masculine Aspirations in Women," deals with the feminine counterpart of the pseudohomosexual conflict in men. In this paper, I subject the wish to be a man to an adaptational analysis and show that it is a symbolic expression of dependency and power needs.

The fifth and sixth papers return to the problem of homosexuality in men. Both papers originally had the same title, "Psychotherapy of Male Homosexuality." The fifth was written in collaboration with Dr. Willard Gaylin and Dr. Herbert Hendin, and the sixth in collaboration with Dr. Gaylin. In this volume portions of the original sixth paper have been incorporated into the fifth because of some overlapping in the original publications. The fifth paper retains the original title. It describes a therapeutic approach derived from the earlier psychodynamic formulations and then takes up prognosis, selection of patients for treatment, and special problems of therapeutic technique. The remaining portion of the sixth paper has been retitled, "Case Studies of Male Homosexuals" and contains descriptions of three successfully treated cases with follow-ups of five or more years.

LIONEL OVESEY

CHAPTER 1

The Homosexual Conflict

An Adaptational Analysis

Introduction

THE concept of homosexuality proposed by Sigmund Freud remains relatively unchanged in most of the psychoanalytic literature of today. The theoretical approach used by Freud in the development of this concept makes it difficult to explain certain phenomena that are a part of the homosexual conflict. The classical Freudian frame of reference is an "instinctual" one. It is overweighted on the constitutional side, underweighted on the sociological side. It ultimately traces behavior to instinctual forces that are inherent, have a fixed ontogenetic course of development, and recapitulate phylogeny. The role of society, although not neglected, is minimized, and it is quite possible for instincts to find behavioral expression purely on a constitutional basis without any significant interaction with the social environment. This is especially true in the case of homosexuality where classical theory pays insufficient attention to those social realities that underlie behavior categorized as homosexual. It is the purpose of this paper to recast the psychodynamics of homosexuality within an adaptational context in order to demonstrate the crucial role of societal forces. The paper will not deal all-inclusively with the problem of homosexuality, but will attempt to develop a particular train of thought in as straight a line as possible. The discussion will be limited to the psychodynamics of male homosexuality, but the basic adaptational thesis is equally applicable to female homosexuality.

Freud's Formulations on Homosexuality.

Let us begin by summarizing those of Freud's formulations on homosexuality that are the more pertinent for this paper.[1] Freud postulated a homosexual stage in the ontogenetic development of the sexual instinct. This stage lay between autoerotism and a heterosexual object-choice. The theory of instincts and its energic equivalent, the libido theory, held that neurotic symptoms represented repression of perverse infantile sexual impulses. If no repression occurred, the perverse impulses remained conscious and found direct expression without displacement. This led to one of Freud's earliest conclusions, that "neurosis is the negative of a perversion," a dictum which of necessity excluded homosexuality from the neuroses and also, at least theoretically, from the realm of psychoanalytic therapy, since only neuroses were believed susceptible to psychoanalysis.

Freud's constitutional orientation led him to adopt the concept of bisexuality. This concept held that each individual was constitutionally endowed with both male and female psychosexual attributes that eventually sought instinctual gratification in terms of object-choice. Freud postulated that in the child the sexual opposites for sexual behavior were at first *activity* as opposed to *passivity*, but without any comprehension by the child of sexual role. As the child discovered the difference between male and female genitals, he came to understand the biological significance of *masculine* and *feminine*. If the child's previous behavior had been active, his subsequent identification was with the masculine sexual role; if passive, with the feminine sexual role. Environmental influences acted through this innate predisposition—that is, a person was born either active-masculine or passive-feminine and he responded to external factors on the basis of these inherent trends. If the predisposition to femininity was strong, fixation of the libido at a homosexual level became mandatory; no environmental influence was necessary. If the predisposition was weak, then strong environmental influence was required to achieve the same effect.

From clinical observation, Freud gradually formulated the classical mechanisms for the development of homosexuality. I have recapitulated the more important of these in the language of the libido theory:

(1) The simplest mechanism for homosexual fixation is also the one most likely to occur on a purely constitutional basis. The individual who resorts to this mechanism shows an excessive erotogenic interest in his own genital during the autoerotic period. Later, when shifting from autoerotism to object-love, he remains at a point of fixation between the two. As a result his partner must have a genital similar to his own for him to feel any sexual attraction. In fantasy he then loves himself through his partner.

(2) A more complicated mechanism has its origin in

castration-anxiety. The patient, following the failure of his oedipal strivings toward his mother, regresses from object-love to narcissistic identification. He introjects the mother, identifies with her incorporated image, and thus magically becomes the object that he cannot possess. He then behaves toward others as previously he had wished his mother to behave toward him. He chooses homosexual love-objects and gives them the love he desired from his mother. Although he acts as if he were his own mother, emotionally he is centered in the homosexual object and thus enjoys being loved by himself.

(3) In those cases in which there is an anal fixation of the libido, in addition to a homosexual fixation, the wish for sexual gratification from the mother becomes transformed into the wish to enjoy it in the same manner as she does, with the father as the love-object. The patient carries out a narcissistic identification with the mother and then submits himself to a father-substitute in a passive-receptive manner.

(4) Another mechanism Freud called "retiring in favor of someone else." This referred to rivalry situations in which the competitive hatred was held in check by transformation into homosexual love. Most often this occurred in rivalry between brothers, occasionally in the rivalry of the son with his father.

These mechanisms all reflect the vicissitudes of the sexual instinct in its search for gratification. They are, of course, adaptational responses, but Freud referred their ultimate explanation internally to instinct rather than externally to social environment. The primary determinant lay in the varying degrees of the original homosexual endowment rather than in the specific life experiences that constituted social reality.

Homosexuality as a Neurosis: An Adaptational Approach

In recent years Freud's concept of homosexuality has been challenged by those workers who discarded the libido theory in favor of a more adaptational approach. This made possible the reclassification of homosexuality as a neurosis and opened pathways to psychotherapy. Rado[2] systematically reappraised the concept of bisexuality and point by point demonstrated its scientific weakness. Horney[3] drew the homosexual into the ambit of the "neurotic personality." Thompson,[4] using Sullivan's operational scheme, described homosexuality as a disordered form of interpersonal relations. Rado[5] reexamined all of sexual behavior, including certain aspects of homosexuality, from an adaptational point of view. All agreed that the indiscriminate label of homosexuality frequently disguised nonsexual elaborations that had to do with dependency, aggression, competition, domination, and submission. All proposed that the term "sexual" be used to designate only that behavior having orgastic satisfaction as its motivational aim, a proposition with which there can be no disagreement.

The adaptational frame of reference interprets psychological behavior as the result of two forces: the needs of the individual and the societal demands. The term "adaptation" refers to the behavioral maneuvers by means of which the individual *adapts* to his social environment as he seeks to insure his survival and to gratify his needs. The primary goal of all behavior is survival. Gratification of nonsurvival needs, under normal circumstances, is always secondary. The normal individual will inevitably give priority to survival in the event of conflict with other needs. Psychological needs may be divided into three categories: (1) the psychophysiological needs, such as the needs for air and water; (2) the psychobiological needs (oral, anal, and sexual); and (3) the culturally-determined psychosocial needs, such as the needs for status and prestige.

Psychophysiological needs are primarily related to the

physical environment and are controlled by internal home-ostatic devices. They do not concern us here. Let us focus on the other two.

We can assume that all normal individuals are innately endowed with approximately similar oral, anal, and sexual needs. Likewise, these needs seek gratification through similar end-goals, but the particular adaptations by means of which these goals are achieved will vary with the social environment. The culturally-determined psychosocial needs are not innate. They develop only after the individual's exposure to the society into which he has been born, and their nature is determined by the demands of that society. Here, too, the adaptations required to satisfy these needs will vary with the social environment. We can therefore conclude that in an adaptational context, in contrast to the instinctual view, the behavior of the individual will vary as his social environment varies. This conclusion is bolstered by cross-cultural analyses, a field of research pioneered by Kardiner.[6] Thus the adaptational frame of reference has a sociological emphasis, as opposed to the constitutional emphasis of the instinctual frame of reference.

The first technique for survival and for need-gratification is dependency. This is an adaptation that is rooted in the biological helplessness of the infant at birth. Clinical studies demonstrate that the adult unconsciously thinks of the infantile period as one of magical control. This must be the way the infant sees himself. He is magically omnipotent and his parents are magical agencies for the satisfaction of his needs. To the extent that the child learns to do for himself as he matures, he gives up his desires for magical (dependency) intervention. The goal of healthy development is a self-sufficient, self-reliant, independent person. Resort to infantile dependency in an

adult is an unerring indicator of a failure in adaptive resources.

How do such failures arise? All important in their
origin is the interaction between dependency and discipline. It is through this interaction that the behavior of
the child is molded in accordance with social demands as
mediated by the parents. The child will abandon important gratifications to insure dependency status. A good
example is infantile sexual activity. Here, excessive parental discipline confronts the child with two great dangers:
physical punishment and the withdrawal of love. The
former is frequently extended in fantasy to imply bodily
mutilation (castration) and death; the latter means loss
of dependency. In either case each is a threat to survival
and the child responds with the emergency emotion of
fear. This fear may be so great as to force a partial or
complete withdrawal from sexual activity. Later, as the
child grows, any sexual situation will revive the earlier
fear, and an inhibition of normal sexual behavior is established. This inhibition of healthy function by fear in
response to an imagined danger is the core of the neurotic
process.

Such an inhibition is the take-off point for a homosexual adaptation. The person reacts with such intense
fear in relation to a heterosexual object that he fails in
heterosexual performance. His sexual need, however, continues unabated and is diverted to a "safer" object. This
object is a homosexual one, and it derives its added safety
from the reassuring presence of the penis, which allays the
patient's castration anxiety. Homosexuality, in this light,
is a deviant form of sexual adaptation into which the
patient is forced by the injection of fear into the normal
sexual function. This, of course, is a general statement
that holds good for any type of sexual psychopathology,

but as of today it is the best that can be offered. We do not know any more about the intrinsic factors that account for homosexuality in one person and not in another than we do about symptom-choice in any other psychic aberration. This homosexual adaptation can be overt and conscious, or it can be latent and either conscious or unconscious. In the former, the person accepts his heterosexual failure and overtly acts out his homosexual impulses; in the latter, he refuses to accept it and either consciously suppresses his homosexual impulses or represses them to the unconscious.

So far, the homosexual mechanisms here described in no way differ from those worked out by Freud, except that they are restated in an adaptational frame of reference without recourse to constitution. It would be simple if this were all there was to the homosexual conflict, but the problem is vastly more complicated. Inhibitions do not stay confined to the behavior area in which they are originally laid down. Unfortunately, the lack of confidence and the drop in self-esteem coincident to any inhibition tend to spread to other activities, and new inhibitions appear. This is particularly true if discipline in general is severe. The end result of such failure in growth is the unconscious retention in adulthood of a dependency adaptation.

Penis = Breast Equation

The dependent person aspires on the most primitive level to recapture the maternal breast. Such persons will have repeated dreams of food, all symbolic of the infantile desire to have one's every need gratified by an all-powerful parent. The breast-fantasy is the most direct reparative approach to the problem of dependency. There is, however, an alternative route; it is based on the equation, *penis = breast*. The root factors behind this equation are extremely complex and appear to originate in the concurrent development of multiple inhibitions in several behavior areas, each of which reinforces the others. In such instances, the inhibition of sexual behavior is central. The person who cannot perform sexually, unconsciously attributes his failure to genital mutilation (castration), the anticipated parental punishment for his sexual transgressions, real or imagined. He then generalizes this castration-fantasy to include all failures of performance, nonsexual as well as sexual. Thus, to put it conversely, the penis becomes the symbol not only of successful sexual performance, but also of mastery in all other areas of behavior; that is, the penis becomes the symbol of total adaptive capacity. Once this has occurred, the person unconsciously conceives of any adaptive failure in terms of injury to his penis. A symbolic reflection of this idea is a concern with penis size: success is equated with a large penis, failure with a small one. The dream of a patient, a lawyer, plagued with fears of performing in the courtroom will illustrate the use of these symbols. The patient had the dream in anticipation of making a speech before the court. In the dream, he began his presentation by opening his fly and taking out his penis, a huge monster of an organ measured in feet instead of inches. He brandished this weapon in a threatening fashion, cowed all before him, and triumphantly delivered his speech amid great acclaim. Dreams of this kind in dependent males are typical. All revolve around success and failure couched in terms of the penis—its size, integrity, and ability to function.

The unconscious ideation outlined above forms the basis for a magical reparative fantasy in which the penis is ultimately equated with the breast. The dependent person, instead of relying on the breast, may achieve the same effect by invoking a compensatory fantasy of oral or anal incorporation of a stronger man's penis, thus undoing his castration and making the donor's strength available to him. As we shall see, this equation as a solution to the problem of dependency is of major significance in the development of an anxiety about homosexuality.

Reparative Infantile Fantasies

Let us examine more closely the reality circumstances under which the dependent adult resorts to these reparative infantile fantasies. Here, certain social configurations become pertinent. Ours is a fiercely competitive culture that is intensely demanding in its pressures for superlative performance. The emphasis invariably falls on *success*, and there is little room for compromise without loss of face. This social ideal is intimately related to our conventional standards for the masculine and feminine sociosexual roles. Masculinity is equated with strength, dominance, superiority; femininity, with weakness, submissiveness, inferiority. The former represents success; the latter failure. It is in this cultural context that Freud's ideas about activity and passivity must be redefined. These two polarities are not constituent parts of a sexual instinct. In fact, they have nothing to do with sexuality as such but are really expressions of the individual's capacity for assertion in any behavior area. In our culture the premium is on self-assertion, and the man who lacks it and fails to meet success-goals is plagued with doubts about his masculinity. Thus any adaptive failure—sexual, social, or vocational—may be perceived unconsciously as a failure in the masculine role and, which is worse, may be symbolically extended through an equation that is calculated only to intensify the anxiety incident to the failure. This equation is the following: *I am a failure = I am castrated = I am not a man = I am a woman = I am a homosexual.*

The operation of this equation can be easily demonstrated in dream material. Consider the following example, the dream of a medical student who missed an easy diagnosis that was subsequently picked up by another member of his group:

It was a scene in front of my childhood house. A tremendous group of people was assembled to greet my arrival. It was like the return of the prodigal son. I was a great celebrity. I drove up in a red Cadillac and everybody began to applaud. There was a Negro porter there, a little colored midget. I got on my knees, took out his penis, and began to kiss it. The crowd hooted in derision. I woke up in disgust. Did it mean I was a fairy?

Here, the patient's aspirations for success were given a sharp blow by his mistake of the day before. This competitive defeat is ultimately symbolized in the dream as a homosexual submission to a person he considered markedly inferior. We see, then, that any failure in assertion in any activity that can conventionally be classified under the heading of "masculinity" may set in motion a dynamic chain of events that can terminate in an anxiety misidentified by the patient as "homosexual." This is the case in the dream. The anxiety is perceived by the patient as a "homosexual" one, but in reality it has to do with competition and status.

The dependent male is engaged in a constant struggle to salvage his self-esteem. He may attempt to deny his weakness by acting out its opposite, a compensatory striving power. Dependency strivings and power strivings can thus be considered opposite sides of the same coin. The power-driven dependent male is overcompetitive and structures relationships with other men in terms of dominance-submission. These relationships are symbolically placed in a male-female context—that is, the weaker male is forced to submit as a woman to the stronger male. For this reason, a failure in competitive performance may suddenly find paranoid expression as a fear of homosexual assault. For example, a patient who was involved in a hostile, competitive transference began to complain that every afternoon a few minutes before his interview he began to suffer a foul taste in his mouth that lasted throughout the hour and disappeared only after he left the therapist's office. This symptom remained unexplained for several weeks until its meaning became clear in a nightmare:

I was sitting on a toilet moving my bowels. It was not an ordinary kind of a toilet. It had a queer tubular shape. As a matter of fact, it was shaped like a penis. I flushed the toilet, but instead of the water going down, it shot up like a geyser. I tried to get off but I could not. Suddenly, I felt something in my mouth and I spat out several brown pellets that I realized were feces. I woke up, terribly frightened, with that awful taste in my mouth.

The foul taste was a hysterical expression of his fear of anal rape, the symbol of competitive defeat by the therapist. The fear disguises a wish for the very act he rejects, because by it he would magically incorporate the therapist's more powerful penis. The oral symptom in this instance is especially interesting since the homosexual attack in the dream is an anal one; usually such a symptom is related to fellatio. The symptom disappeared immediately upon interpretation of the dream.

These are the interactions between the dependent male and his social environment that recapitulate the infantile castration and revive in him the infantile reparative fantasies of incorporating a stronger man's penis. These fantasies, motivationally, need have nothing to do with homosexuality, but because mechanically they involve a physical act that can also be used for homosexual purposes, they serve only to accentuate the anxiety they were designed to dissipate. It is a case of the cure being worse than the disease. A pertinent example is that of a patient who complained of repetitive fantasies in which he performed fellatio always on the same man, his uncle. These fantasies produced a most unpleasant affect and led to self-referential ideas of femininity. It was possible in therapy to pinpoint the occurrence of the fantasies in relation to the situation that provoked them. The patient was a young executive who had risen quickly to a position of prominence in a giant business organization. He was instrumental in the procurement of new business, and it was at these times, when success or failure was in balance and the pressure upon him was great, that the fantasies appeared. The choice of the uncle as the magical donor was not accidental. The patient was a short man, only five feet six, while the uncle was six feet three and a fabulously successful business tycoon to boot.

One final example will serve to nail down with remarkable clarity the interrelationships between social goals, failure of performance, and magical repair. It is the dream of a college instructor who lost out to a younger rival in promotion to a professorship:

I was sitting in a theater waiting for the show to begin. The management announced there was a celebrity in the audience. A man got up and went to the stage where he was introduced as a world-famous figure. He got a big hand and then I realized it was my rival. I felt very depressed. Finally, the curtain went up and it was a burlesque act, a chase. A small comedian with baggy pants came running from the wing carrying a small wooden sword in his hand. After him came a bigger man with a bigger sword, and after him came a still bigger man with a still bigger sword. Suddenly, the second man goosed the first man with his sword and it came out in front pushing up the small man's pants just like a penis. The audience thought this was terribly funny and roared with laughter. Then the third man goosed the second, but the sword, instead of coming out in the second man's pants, came out like a huge penis in the first man's pants. Now the audience really laughed. This was even funnier. I woke up laughing.

Here, again, the competitive defeat is perceived as a homosexual attack, but at the same time it is turned to reparative use through the magical acquisition of the victorious opponent's penis. The patient resorts to laughter, a mechanism of denial, to disguise his humiliation.

Motivational Goals of the Homosexual Conflict

Behavior, to be understandable to the observer, must be defined in terms of motivational goals. Nowhere is this more true than in the case of the homosexual conflict. This conflict, as we have seen, can be broken down into three component parts: sexual, dependency, and power. Only the first is truly sexual in its motivation. The other two are not sexual at all, although they make use of the sexual apparatus to achieve their ends. They are in reality *pseudohomosexual* components of the homosexual conflict. All three components exist in varying strengths in different persons, and which component is in the ascendency at any given time can be inferred only from the motivational context in which the person's behavior becomes manifest. Variable combinations of these ingredients provide an adaptational formula by means of which the behavior of any particular person suffering from a homosexual conflict, either overt or hidden, can be understood.

In the overt homosexual, the sexual component is primary, and the primary motivational goal is therefore orgastic satisfaction. The dependency and power components are secondary, but nevertheless extremely important, because by their relative strengths they will determine the psychosocial structure of the homosexual relationship as well as the physical mechanics of the homosexual act. The overt homosexual in whom the dependency component is markedly strong gives up all pretense of meeting the requirements of the masculine role. He dramatizes his failure by the cultivation of quasi-feminine traits that he uses as bait to attract his preferred object-choice—the stronger, more "masculine" male. He makes of his partner a parent and sets up a parent-child relationship in which he aspires to be the child. For him, the major adventitious purpose of the homosexual act is dependency-gratification, and, therefore, physically he gravitates toward fellatio and anal mount with himself each time on the recipient end. In this manner, magically, through the incorporation of his partner's penis, he repairs his own adaptive deficiencies.

What about the "masculine" male who is homosexually attracted to his more "feminine" counterpart? Here, also, the sexual component is primary, but of the other two, the power component takes precedence over the dependency component. This person, adaptationally, is better integrated than his partner. He is driven to gratify his sexual need in a homosexual fashion because he is too frightened to perform heterosexually, but, notwithstanding, he rejects any representation of himself as feminine. His object-choice is a man, but one as much like a woman as possible. If, in addition, the power component is strong, he attempts to redeem his masculine failure through a compensatory domination of his weaker partner. He seeks to have men submit to his penis orally and anally, but generally refuses to accept the reverse role. He denies his own dependency at the expense of the weaker man. In this way he not only satisfies himself sexually, but also enhances his deflated masculinity by making a woman out of his partner. The homosexual act itself is a confession of masculine failure, yet in this instance the patient paradoxically uses it to affirm his masculinity. Cases of this kind could well be labeled "paradoxical homosexuality."

The "feminine" male and the "masculine" male represent two extremes of the overt homosexual conflict. There can be all degrees of variation in between, and it is possible for relationships to be on a greater level of equality. This is more apt to occur when the pseudohomosexual components are less weighted. The union is then joined mainly for purposes of sexual gratification and each partner does for the other what he would have the other do for him. The activity of choice in such relationships is more often mutual masturbation. Fellatio and anal mount occur less frequently, and then primarily as alternative forms of sexual stimulation rather than as reparative devices. In these types of homosexuals, the extent of "feminine" dramatization or of "masculine" protest in their social behavior will be determined, as it is in the more extreme types, by the relative strengths of the pseudohomosexual components.

Pseudohomosexual Conflict

I have previously referred to the latent homosexual as one in whom the homosexual impulse was either conscious or unconscious, but not overtly acted out. Here, the term "latent" was applied to the purely sexual component of the conflict. Strictly speaking, this is the only correct application of the term. Anxiety integrated on this basis is a true homosexual anxiety, and it, alone, warrants the label of latent homosexuality. Clinically, however, such anxieties are infrequent. The great majority of so-called homosexual anxieties are motivated by strivings for dependency and power. These anxieties, as has been shown, stem from pseudohomosexual fantasies that are misinterpreted by the patient as being evidences of frank homosexuality. In reality, the sexual component, if present at all, is very much in abeyance. More often it appears to be entirely absent. In these cases, where the homosexual motivation is nonexistent, or so negligible as to have no significant impact, it would be better to drop the term "latent homosexuality" altogether and refer instead to "the pseudohomosexual conflict."

The correct breakdown of the homosexual conflict into its motivational components is of primary importance in psychotherapy. It is here, particularly, that the classical constitutional approach can do great damage. The interpretation of overt homosexuality as an expression of inherent bisexuality is discouraging enough, but to explain dependency and power strivings to a heterosexual patient on the same basis can be catastrophic. Adding fuel is no way to put out a fire. It is hoped that the adaptational analysis of the homosexual conflict as proposed in this chapter will find practical application in the conduct of therapy.

CHAPTER 2

The Pseudohomosexual Anxiety

Introduction

ANXIETIES about homosexuality, when subjected to an adaptational analysis, can be broken down into three motivational components—sexual, dependency, and power. The theoretical basis for such a breakdown has been described in the previous chapter. The sexual component is the only one of these three that seeks sexual gratification as its motivational goal. The anxiety generated in this search is, therefore, a true homosexual anxiety and should be so labeled. Likewise, the associated conflict should be called the homosexual conflict. The dependency and power components, however, as denoted by their names, seek completely different, nonsexual goals, but make use of the genital organs to achieve them. Although the goals appear to be sexual, in reality they are not. For this reason, I have designated these two components as *pseudohomosexual*. The anxiety incident to their operation constitutes the pseudohomosexual anxiety—that is, an anxiety about dependency and power strivings that is misinterpreted by the patient as a true homosexual anxiety. Here the conflict should be called the pseudohomosexual conflict as distinguished from the true homosexual conflict.

A Case Study of Pseudohomosexuality

This chapter consists of a case study that provides clinical documentation for the concept of pseudohomosexuality. The purpose of this chapter is twofold: first, to demonstrate the adaptational psychodynamics behind the pseudohomosexual anxiety; and second, to demonstrate the practical application of these psychodynamics in the conduct of psychotherapy. No attempt will be made to describe the case in its every minute detail. Instead, the voluminous material has been edited and organized in such a way as to achieve economically the purposes of the paper. The emphasis will be on psychodynamics rather than on the technical subtleties of therapy, but enough of the technique will be described to make clear the relation between the two. The power component emerges as the central conflict in this case, and I have organized my discussion around it. However, in due course, I will also point out the significance of the dependency component and show its relationship to the central conflict. There is nothing unique about the psychopathology in the case to be presented here. Any one of a number of cases of pseudohomosexuality could have been used, although it is true, of course, that each would have had singular features peculiar to the individual patient. The selection of this particular case for demonstration was based on the remarkable clarity of the patient's productions, which resulted from a rare combination of qualities—high intelligence, creative imagination, lively emotionality, and psychological aptitude. The patient was in treatment for two years. He was seen four times a week during the first six months, three times a week during the second six months, and twice a week during the second year, for a total of 230 treatment hours. There were three short lapses in his visits of a few weeks each during this two-year period. The treatment was conducted in accordance with the adaptational technique of psychoanalytic therapy with the patient lying on the couch.[1]

The patient was a 30-year-old married male of medium but athletic build, cleancut and personable. He was completely masculine in his appearance, manner of dress, gestures, and voice. There was nothing about him that would even remotely suggest the effeminate. He spoke fluently and related easily to the therapist. He was employed at a minimum salary in a trainee capacity as an assistant to a minor executive in a large business organization. His wife also worked in a job that had about equal status and brought in about the same amount of money. They lived modestly and needed both jobs to make ends meet. There were no children. Diagnostically, the patient was a neurotic; the question of a psychosis did not seriously arise.

The patient sought psychotherapy because of a marital problem. For the past two years he had felt a constant, unreasoning resentment of mounting intensity toward his wife, although he readily conceded that her behavior was exemplary and in no way provocative. Together with this resentment he had experienced a loss of sexual interest with a gradual decline in his ability to achieve an erection, whereas previously in his marriage he had been fully potent. He had

had intercourse only twice in the last six months and then both times he had found it necessary to be drunk in order to carry through. He complained also of chronic anxiety, feelings of depression, and insomnia. He had been falling back on alcohol more and more to relieve his sleeplessness and this he felt had become a serious problem. Hardly a night passed that he did not drink himself to sleep. His emotional withdrawal from his wife had led to a steady deterioration of the marriage and she was about ready to give up. It was primarily at her insistence, in a final effort to save the relationship, that he came to the psychiatrist. These were the immediate problems, but behind them were lifelong feelings of inadequacy, inferiority, and lack of confidence.

The patient was an only child, born and raised in a small New England town. His mother, a housewife, was a strange mixture, a domineering but overprotective and affectionate woman, who set exorbitant standards for performance. He had to be the best in everything—an impossible task—and his childhood was a nightmare of failure, recrimination, and exhortation to do better. The mother was very emotional, and her appeals for improvement were often accompanied by extravagant displays of weeping and wailing. His father was a country doctor who spent little time at home. He rarely showed interest in his son; when he did, it was usually to make an adverse comment. The patient puts it this way: "My father was never around. There was no bond between us. We spoke as strangers. He never believed I could do anything, and when I did do something he regarded it as a happy accident, a pleasant surprise. Father regarded my failures as norms." The patient's childhood otherwise was typical of that of any American boy growing up in a small town. He engaged in the usual school and social activities, but always felt himself inadequate in comparison with other members of his group. He began masturbation in early adolescence and continued into adulthood. He attended college for three years, and during this time had his initial heterosexual experiences. These were sporadic and few in number and usually terminated in a premature ejaculation. At no time was there any history of homosexual relations. The war came, and he left college before graduation to become a fighter pilot in the Air Force. Shortly before leaving this country, he married a girl two years his junior. He was able to stay with his wife for only a few months, but his sexual adjustment during this period was completely satisfactory. Overseas he flew many missions, all in single-engine fighter planes, for which he received several decorations for valor in combat. He returned from the war and immediately took a training job with a civilian airline as a pilot of four-engine aircraft, a type he had never flown before. He was discharged after a few months because he repeatedly failed the instrument check. He then reentered college for a year, took his degree, and obtained his present job through the intervention of his wife's relatives who exercised influence in the firm. The symptoms for which he came to treatment broke out after his failure with the airline.

The patient opened therapy with a recitation of his "failures" during his childhood years. Two of many examples will suffice, since any one is similar to all the others. In the sixth grade he began to do poorly in arithmetic. His mother, in a characteristic fashion, arranged that he stay after school for special tutelage: "Mother would take me to the instructor and in the presence of both I was very embarrassed and couldn't possibly grasp it, but I acted as though I did. What a dolt I was! He must have thought I was awful dumb!" About the same time his mother insisted he take piano lessons. He rebelled on the grounds his friends would call him a sissy, but as always his mother's will prevailed. Here again he suffered: "I had to learn special pieces to play at the recitals, but knowing I had to play at a public gathering,

I couldn't learn them. I never had a time of greater embarrassment. It was just a matter of getting through before dying of fright. I worried for hours before playing, and then I would hack the piece completely." These two episodes are typical, and for several sessions the patient continued in this vein. He recollected an astounding total of childhood incidents, all couched in identical terms of failure. Not once did he mention a single item that he considered a success. After he had disposed of his childhood, he went on to his college years and subjected them to the same treatment. Here his concern was mainly with women and his rivalry for their favor. In his view all the other men were socially graceful, dated only the prettiest girls, and invariably seduced them; he, however, was a boor, got stuck with the crows, and rarely slept with anybody. In the Army, too, he could not act the role he felt he should. He addressed all superior officers as "sir" or by rank, even overseas where informality reigned and where first names were used except for the highest grades. He felt it would have been presumptuous for someone of his low stature to do otherwise.

This deference to authority continued to plague him in his current job. His immediate superior was a petty tyrant who stepped on the patient to inflate his own importance. The patient was full of good ideas, but his boss appropriated all of them and then took the credit. On the other hand, when the boss made an error, it was the patient who was accused to the authorities higher up. The patient had borne this intimidation in silence, too fearful to assert an effective protest. Such a protest would have been completely feasible because of his family connections in the firm and in no way would have put his job in jeopardy. The realization of his weakness deflated him thoroughly: "I know I must stand up and have courage and not let myself be victimized by him or by people like him. Unless I learn to do that, I will never feel like a man." He had no sooner said this than he became apprehensive, fell silent, and began to tremble. Finally, he remarked it was ridiculous, but he felt as though he were in great danger. It was like a combat mission, the moment before approaching the target. That night he had a nightmare.

Dream One.—I was standing in a bull ring with a man I could not identify, someone uninitiated to bull-fighting. The matador had gotten hurt. He was on the ground, and the bull was goring him. Blood was everywhere. The picadors with their capes were trying to draw the bull away from the matador. I was explaining all this to the person with me, whoever he was. I said that as soon as the bull was gotten away, they would give first aid to the matador. I hoped it wouldn't be too late.

The bull, he felt, was his boss, but, as will be pointed out, it could equally well represent any other strong superior male. He was not only himself in the dream, but also the matador; and the uninitiated man was the therapist. In the dream he unconsciously explains to the therapist the motivational basis for his paralysis in competitive relationships with other men. The difficulty lies in his symbolic conceptions of assertion and aggression.

It would be helpful here to pause for a moment and define these terms. Assertion, as used in this paper, is a generic term that encompasses all behavior, with or without hostile intent, designed to gratify a need. Aggression is a specific form of assertion that has hostile intent toward an impeding object and seeks to injure or destroy it. Aggression has a wide range of action from the completely nonviolent, such as a verbal lacing, to the most violent, such as murder.

In the present case, the patient unconsciously sees all aggression solely in terms of murderous violence for which he expects retaliation in kind. He then generalizes this concept to include, without discrimination, any and all forms of self-assertion, nonaggressive as well as aggressive. Such a dynamism, through the fear of retaliation, effectively blocks off efforts at assertion. In a symbolically violent exchange of this kind the patient cannot possibly win. His deflated self-image inevitably puts him in the weaker position, and retaliation from the stronger rival is certain. He, therefore, inhibits assertion in order literally to save his life; or to put it conversely, he conceives of assertion as an invitation to suicide. This inhibition, as will be shown later in the paper, stems developmentally from his one-sided submissive relationship with his father. The dream also has unconscious homosexual implications for the patient, but since he made no mention of homosexuality in his associations, the therapist's interpretation of the dream was limited to pointing out the patient's misconceptions about assertion.

There is still another element that is hidden in the dream. This is a transference element that goes beyond the therapist's overt appearance as the uninitiated bystander. The therapist, too, is symbolized by the bull, and the patient's anxiety on the couch the previous day was just as much in reference to the therapist as to the patient's boss, but since the patient did not bring this up, the transference, like the question of homosexuality, was left untouched.

The patient for the next few weeks was preoccupied with the problem of assertion. His unconscious misconceptions were pointed out to him by the therapist over and over again in every situation in which they appeared, past and present. He was not as yet encouraged to assert himself, but finally one day he spontaneously announced he would submit to intimidation no longer. Next time he would speak back to the boss. The next time came, but unhappily, the patient had made his vow too soon. He felt powerless as always and said nothing. He symbolized this failure in a humiliating but revealing dream.

Dream Two.—I tore into his office madder than hell. He was sitting behind his desk. This time I was really going to tell him. He looked up and said, "What in hell do you want?" I just stood there and couldn't say anything. Then I turned around, but instead of walking away, I crawled away on my hands and feet with my ass up in the air.

This unbecoming simian-like posture is a measure of his humiliation, but it is also something more. It is a symbol of "feminine" submission to the dominant male.* It reveals a new factor in the patient's unconscious conception of competitive relations between men. These relationships are placed in a male-female context in which the weaker male is castrated by the stronger male and then forced to submit to him as a woman. This submission is generally conceived as a rape, usually anal, occasionally oral. For this reason, a competitive defeat, the result of a failure in assertion, can be misinterpreted by

* The term *simian* is used advisedly. There is a striking similarity between the patient's behavior in the dream and the behavior of male apes defeated in combat by other males. The weaker ape, in token of his defeat, submissively assumes the coital position of the female, and presents his buttocks to the stronger, victorious ape.[2] The feminine presentation here is believed to be *social* in its motivation, rather than sexual, and is an indicator of social submission. This is exactly the position assumed by the patient in the dream. It would be tempting to speculate philosophically on the evolutionary significance of this dream-image, but such speculation is beyond the scope of this paper.

the defeated male as evidence of homosexuality even though the area of struggle may be completely nonsexual. The appearance of this symbol in the dream heralded for the patient an acute outbreak of pseudohomosexual anxiety. The most likely expression of this anxiety is in the form of a paranoid projection; that is, a fear of homosexual assault. This projection is more obvious in Dream Three, to be related later, and in the patient's associations to that dream. In his associations to Dream Two, just related, the patient spoke only of his humiliation. As with the previous dream he said nothing of homosexuality and, therefore, again, this subject was left untouched.

The unpleasant bottoms-up image, provoked by the failure of his resolve, ushered in a period of resistance. He had many silences and complained he had no thoughts. He dreamt that the therapist was a criminal and the therapy was dangerous and ahead of him lay only disaster. Then, gingerly, he began to talk of his marriage, a topic he had assiduously avoided since the initial interview. He recounted the early days of the relationship between himself and his wife:

The patient was very much in love with his wife and she with him in the early part of their marriage. All went well at first. Even sex, in spite of his premarital difficulties, was no problem. Then he failed with the airline and seemingly overnight everything changed. He returned to school, and she had to get a job. It embarrassed him that she was working. It seemed the least a man could do was support his wife. He felt ashamed before her family and her friends and began to avoid them. At the same time he began to withdraw from her. Suddenly, he noticed all kinds of things about his wife that had never impressed him before. For one thing, she no longer seemed attractive. He had always thought of her as a beautiful woman, but now she ceased to look feminine. She took on a decidedly masculine cast. She had always had some hair on her lip and also around her nipples. This had never bothered him before, but now it repelled him. As soon as he got into bed with her all he could see was this hair, and he would have the thought it was like going to bed with a man. Then he felt a great hatred, and, of course, he promptly lost his erection. It wasn't long before the prospect of having intercourse with her became so unpalatable that he stopped even making the attempt. He noticed, too, that he was ashamed to be seen in public with his wife. He had been proud to show her off, but now he felt people wondered how he ever got stuck with her, although nobody ever said anything. It was during this period, while he went to school and his wife worked to support them, that he experienced a maximum sense of failure. Finally, he graduated from college and got a job, but this didn't seem to make much difference. He was glad to get it, but it lacked status, and worst of all, it paid so little his wife had to go on working.

It took several sessions to relate this story of his marriage. He terminated the account on a note of complete disparagement: He was without question the most inadequate male the world had ever seen.

At this point, the patient had another nightmare:

Dream Three.—Some big guy, a great big bruiser with a crew cut, was chasing me. I tried to escape but he caught me and before I knew it he had my shirt off. He took a cigarette and lit it and stuck the lighted end into my stomach. I yelled for help.

He quickly gave a dual identification of his assailant. At first it looked like the therapist, though a considerably enlarged version of him, but then he was reminded of a fraternity brother from college, a marvelous athlete known in fraternity circles as "Stud." This name proclaimed the size of his penis that by general acknowledgement was the largest on Fraternity Row. One day a group of students prevailed upon this man to expose himself for purposes of measurement. This he did, first flaccid, then erect, and in the latter state somebody suddenly grabbed the penis and masturbated it to climax on the spot, to the great amusement of everyone present. The lone exception was the patient who saw nothing funny and experienced only shame and disgust. From this association he went on to remember a homosexual overture, totally unexpected, from an instructor in college—an overture he had indignantly rejected. The patient then confessed he frequently worried that he might be a homosexual, although he was unaware of erotic feelings toward men, nor had he ever engaged in homosexual activity. He also worried that people thought him effeminate, although he could point to no instance where he was so accused. He recognized that the dream represented a homosexual assault—anal mount came to his mind—but he could not explain what at this time prompted him to dream it.

The explanation is not difficult if it is cast in adaptational rather than in instinctual terms. The answer does not lie in the vicissitudes of a sexual instinct nor in a feminine component of a constitutional bisexuality. In fact, motivationally, the dream has nothing whatsoever to do with sex. Rather, the patient makes use of a homosexual act to symbolize an adaptive failure in a completely different area of behavior. The dream is the end result of a dynamic sequence of ideas related to one another through a symbolic, but logical equation. The situation of origin for this equation is the marital relationship. The trouble began, as was noted, with his failure as a pilot. His return to school while his wife went to work represented to him a reversal in the conventional mascu-line-feminine socioeconomic roles. He reacted to this reversal in a completely literal fashion—that is, his wife became the man and he became the woman. Symbolically then, what in actuality was purely a socioeconomic change, became for him an alteration in gender. It is this failure in masculine assertion that sets the equation in motion and carries it through the following sequence: *I am a failure = I am not a man = I am castrated = I am a woman = I am a homosexual.* The feminine identification in this equation in patients with a more malignant pathology can be the starting point for the delusion of femininity. Fortunately, this patient never got that far but contented himself with vague feelings of reference. The terminal idea in this series generates a pseudohomosexual anxiety—that is, an anxiety misinterpreted by the patient as homosexual in its motivational origin when in reality he is concerned with a failure in nonsexual assertion. The defense against this anxiety is the paranoid projection that gives rise to the dream.

The correct breakdown of an anxiety into its motivational components is crucial to the conduct of a dynamic psychotherapy. It is, therefore, extremely important in order to interpret this dream that one have clearly in mind just what motivational impulses are being projected. Instinctual theory would explain the dream in terms of so-called latent homosexuality. The projected impulse in this instance would be the desire for homosexual gratification. This is the classical formula originally proposed by Freud.[3] It begins with the idea, "I want to have homosexual relations with him," and it ends with the projection of this idea, "He wants to have homosexual relations with me." In adaptational terms, however, sexual desire as a motivational factor does not enter into it. What, then, is being projected? First, let us summarize: the patient has had a failure in nonsexual assertion to which he has symbolically reacted as evidence of homosexuality, and then, still symbolically, has defended himself through a projected homosexual attack. At all times, however, his primary concern is with assertion, its effects and countereffects, and not with the sexual symbol. The true nature of the projected impulse becomes understandable if one remembers that the patient conceives of any assertion as a piece of violent aggression against his competitors. This is true even though during the assertion he may not be engaged in any actual competition. No matter what he does, the effort is always conceived in competitive terms. For this reason any failure in assertion is experienced as a competitive defeat and exposes him to retaliation. What is projected in this dream is a parallel series of symbolic ideas that reflect this failure, and together with it, the expected retaliation. These ideas are shown in Table I.

TABLE I

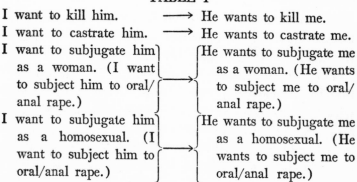

I want to kill him. ⟶ He wants to kill me.

I want to castrate him. ⟶ He wants to castrate me.

I want to subjugate him as a woman. (I want to subject him to oral/anal rape.) ⟶ He wants to subjugate me as a woman. (He wants to subject me to oral/anal rape.)

I want to subjugate him as a homosexual. (I want to subject him to oral/anal rape.) ⟶ He wants to subjugate me as a homosexual. (He wants to subject me to oral/anal rape.)

Not one of these ideas is motivated by sexual desire. The motivation for all is power, sparked by the fear of domination by a superior male competitor. The first two ideas are concerned with the total destruction or the incapacitating injury of the rival, the last two with his social humiliation and degradation. Now it was possible to demonstrate to the patient the dynamic interconnections between the three dreams. First, he was told flatly, without equivocation, that he was not a homosexual. This is a necessary step in the therapeutic management of the pseudohomosexual conflict, and the earlier the material lends itself to such a statement, the better. The purpose of this move is to deflate the neurotic anxiety as quickly as possible and thus facilitate its correct interpretation. Next, over a period of several sessions, the psychodynamics including the transference, exactly as they have been presented in Table I but with one exception, were reviewed with him. The exception has to do with castration as a form of retaliation. No material related to this idea had as yet emerged in his conscious associations and, therefore, the inclusion of this concept in the interpretation was necessarily deferred. The interpretation given had the desired therapeutic effect. The anxiety greatly diminished, the drinking stopped, and he began to fall asleep at night. He even began to feel more kindly toward his wife. This optimistic note marked the end of the first six months of therapy.

The patient was so encouraged by his improvement that he broached the possibility of resuming intercourse with his wife. This revival of sexual interest in his marriage promptly provoked an Oedipal trend that culminated in a frankly incestual dream. The oedipal material, in turn, touched off a spate of unpleasant early memories about his father. He recalled with great bitterness his father's low opinion of him and his own futile attempts at rebuttal. Here, even his dreams failed him. These became more and more openly competitive, but the conviction of inferiority was still too fixed, and, in the end, no matter how hard he tried, his father always won out. The struggle between the two was unconsciously expressed in genital symbols: the big penis versus the little penis. An example of such representation is the following dream:

Dream Four.—An airport ramp with a large airplane on it. I am pushing out a small biplane, tail first. Suddenly, I see the large plane has its wing in such a position I won't clear it. I yell, "Heads up!" Too late! My tail hits the wing of the bigger plane, but no damage is done.

The dream underlines the father's invulnerability to competitive attack. This symbolization through penis-size of the capacity for assertion is typical of the power-driven but inhibited male and can give rise to magical reparative fantasies of oral and anal incorporation of a stronger man's penis. No such fantasies appeared during the treatment of this patient, but in all likelihood they were present and perhaps could have been exposed had treatment continued for a longer time. These fantasies are concerned motivationally with the gratification of dependency needs and are based on the equation, *penis* = *breast*. The development and operation of this sort of reparative fantasy are described in the first chapter. The symbolic significance of the tail in the above dream was not yet clear to the patient.

The next dream focused more sharply on this symbol and for the first time brought the castration theme very close to conscious awareness:

Dream Five.—I was playing ball on the high school athletic field. I had a premonition of disaster and looked into the sky. A fighter plane was coming down tail first. It was having engine trouble. Just before it hit the ground the tail came up and the plane smashed flat. The pilot climbed out unhurt. I thought to myself, "It's better to make a belly landing if it will save your tail."

The competitive tone of the dream is set by the athletic field. This dream restates the earlier bottoms-up thesis but makes use of different symbols. He says, in effect, it is better to submit to the superior male than to risk retaliation, in this instance, castration. The patient's associations included the following: "The tail is the directional and guiding instrument of the whole airplane. I'd rather get my wing shot up any day than my tail. Boy, you lose that and you got no rudders, no nothing! You're finished!" Substitute "penis" for "tail" and a major reason for his competitive anxiety becomes obvious. The castration theme emerged without disguise a few days later in a harrowing but extremely graphic dream. The stimulus was a chance incident in the night. He had gone to bed as usual but was awakened shortly after he fell asleep by the romantic yowls of a tom-cat trying to attract a mate. Suddenly there was a shot, then silence. He returned to sleep and had the following nightmare:

Dream Six.—I was sleeping in the fraternity house in college. I heard this cat in great pain. I looked out the window and here was this wretched black beast injured horribly in some way. He was screaming in terrible pain. There was a lot of blood pouring out of his rectum. It was more than that. The cat had a great hole in him through his crotch. He was all torn up. I jumped out of bed and shouted: "Why doesn't someone put that beast out of its misery?"

The tomcat that had prompted the dream had been slain presumably for seeking a sexual partner. The patient's unconscious identification with this cat revived the hidden infantile fantasies of punishment for sexual transgression. The stage had been set for this revival by the gradual emergence of competitive material in relation to his father. He himself spontaneously arrived at the correct answer to the nightmare with a few quick associations. First, he thought of the fraternity house. It brought to mind the homosexual episode previously described. Then he identified the cat as himself. Next, he remarked that he had a pet cat, a black one. It was a spayed male. Here, he had the sudden flash of insight. A spayed male was a castrated male and that must be the way he thought of himself: a woman, a homosexual, a castrated male. It remained only to tie together for him the castration-anxiety, the oedipus complex, and the inhibition of assertion. He was shown that developmentally the first situation of competition was with his father. This competition derived from the Oedipus complex, and the anticipated paternal retaliation consisted of death, castration, and anal rape. He conceived of the original competition as sexual in its nature, but he then extended the concept of punishment to encompass nonsexual competition as well. The end result was the inhibition of assertion with which he had become so familiar.

This last discussion brought the psychodynamics of the central conflict completely into the open. This ended the first year of therapy. The patient could now be encouraged in appropriate assertion. He embarked upon a sustained attempt to reestablish his sexual potency and to resolve his inhibition of aggression. Every effort was made by the therapist to support these attempts. He resumed intercourse with his wife and after a few initial failures gradually regained his potency. The marriage, however, did not hold together. Too much damage had been done, and in the end the couple agreed amicably to separate. Each has since remarried. The problem with aggression proved more difficult than that with sex. Its resolution was equally successful, but took a good deal longer. The focal point for his reeducation became his relationship with the minor executive who was his boss. He refused to accept blame for the latter's mistakes and began to claim credit for any stolen ideas. He became more and more bold in his resistance and eventually carried the fight all the way to the higher authorities. Finally, one day, he came to therapy in great excitement. His boss had been fired, but not only that, the patient had been given the job and with a commensurate raise in salary. The boost in self-esteem and self-confidence can well be imagined. He had jousted with his father, as it were, and had emerged the victor, alive, undamaged, and with his genital intact. It was not long thereafter that the therapy was brought to a successful close. A follow-up interview three years later revealed a further consolidation of his therapeutic gains. There had been no return of symptoms, his new marriage was going well, and he had advanced still higher in his vocation.

This chapter has demonstrated the great importance of a correct motivational breakdown in the therapeutic management of an anxiety about homosexuality. In this particular case, the anxiety was strictly a pseudohomosexual anxiety; a true homosexual motivation was never observed. It is essential, however, to grasp that even if a homosexual motivation had been present it would not have excluded the coexistence of the pseudohomosexual conflict. True homosexuality has a dynamic of its own that stems from similar developmental sources, but it must be analyzed as an independent entity in its own right. In other words a homosexual motivation would simply have created still another problem; it would in no way have obviated the pseudohomosexual problem already present.

The motivational breakdown used in the understanding and treatment of this case was made within an adaptational frame of reference. The instinctual frame of reference does not easily permit such a breakdown because it makes mandatory an interpretation based on the concept of constitutional bisexuality. It is difficult to conceive how a purely instinctual approach could be therapeutically successful. The patient would have to be told of his innate feminine component and the latent homosexuality that went with it and urged to come to terms with both. He would be subjected to this exhortation in spite of the fact that no erotic homosexual intent could be attributed to him. Such an interpretation is completely unrelated to the reality in which the patient finds himself and serves only to intensify the very anxiety it is designed to alleviate. It fails completely to provide the patient with any therapeutically useful motivational insight into his behavior. Pseudohomosexuality is a disorder where the frame of reference, adaptational as opposed to instinctual, can mean the difference between therapeutic success and therapeutic failure.

CHAPTER 3

Pseudohomosexuality, the Paranoid Mechanism, and Paranoia

An Adaptational Revision
of a Classical Freudian Theory

Introduction

THE classical psychoanalytic theory of paranoia in the male was first proposed by Freud in his celebrated paper on the Schreber case.[1] This theory is formulated within an instinctual frame of reference and is based on the concept of constitutional bisexuality. It holds that the paranoid delusion in its various forms is a defense against repressed homosexual impulses. Many subsequent papers have been written by the adherents of Freud in support of this theory, and it has remained essentially unaltered with the passage of time. It has been extended to include nondelusional paranoid responses in the neurotic, and it has also been applied to paranoia in women, but with somewhat less conviction than in the case of men. The theory has found widespread acceptance in psychiatric circles, and most psychiatrists today would probably subscribe quite uncritically to the Freudian proposition that there is an exclusive etiological relationship between paranoia and homosexuality.

Such unanimity is particularly remarkable in view of the repeated observation that cases of paranoia not infrequently fail to show evidence of a homosexual motivation, either in their conscious or their unconscious productions. In such cases, Freud's theory is nevertheless invoked with the implication that the homosexual impulses are really present, but are so deeply repressed that they cannot be uncovered. This discrepancy has been noted by many clinicians, but subjected to formal investigation by only a few. Of special significance is a study by Klein and Horowitz,[2] who searched for homosexual content in the case records of a large number of hospitalized paranoid patients of both sexes who had undergone psychotherapy. The investigators classified as homosexual content not only erotic homosexual needs, feelings, and conflicts, but also fears of being considered homosexual, fears of being or becoming homosexual, and fears of homosexual attack. Their findings are extremely revealing. To begin with, such content was found in only one-fifth of the total group; furthermore, within this fraction, even at the height of illness, most of the patients neither showed any behavior of a homosexual nature nor expressed during treatment any erotic homosexual feelings, in spite of the fact that many of these patients were so disorganized that effective defense would seem impossible. The authors draw the following conclusion, which

is pertinent to the adaptational orientation of this chapter:
"In many patients the fear of being or becoming homosexual was an expression of failure, blow to pride, or
general distrust of acceptance. These fears did not of
necessity represent homosexual strivings."[3] This conclusion is completely in accord with the concept of pseudohomosexuality as I have developed it in the two previous
chapters.

This chapter will present an adaptational revision of
the Freudian theory of paranoia through the application
of the concept of pseudohomosexuality, and will include
those extensions of the original theory that deal with nondelusional manifestations of the paranoid mechanism. I
shall demonstrate that the paranoid phenomena can stem
from nonsexual adaptations to societal stimuli, and motivationally need have nothing to do with homosexuality
whatsoever.

The Freudian Theory of Paranoia

Before presenting my own revision, I should like to
review Freud's essential formulations on the mechanism
of paranoia as they are proposed in his discussion of the
Schreber case. The basic premise is stated by Freud in
the following quotation: "We consider, then, that what
lies at the core of the conflict in cases of paranoia among
males is a homosexual wish-phantasy of *loving a man.*"
He goes on to show that the principal forms of paranoia
can all be represented as contradictions of the single
proposition, "I (a man) *love him* (a man)":[4]

(1) *The delusion of persecution* contradicts the *verb:*
"I do not *love* him—I *hate* him." The latter idea is transformed by projection into another one: "He *hates* (persecutes) *me,* which will justify me in hating him." Thus,
the final formula is: "I do not *love* him—I *hate* him, be-

cause HE PERSECUTES ME." Freud concludes: "Observation leaves room for no doubt that the persecutor is some one who was once loved."

(2) *Erotomania* contradicts the *object:* "I do not love *him*—I love *her*." Projection transforms this formulation into: "I do not love *him*—I love *her*, because SHE LOVES ME."

(3) *The delusion of jealousy* contradicts the *subject:* "It is not *I* who *love* the man—*she* loves him." Freud completes this formulation with the explanation: ". . . and he suspects the woman in relation to all the men whom he himself is tempted to love." Delusions of jealousy in women, he feels, are exactly analogous.

(4) *Megalomania* contradicts the proposition as a whole: "*I do not love at all—I do not love anyone.*" Freud concludes: "And since, after all, one's libido must go somewhere, this proposition seems to be the psychological equivalent of the proposition: 'I love only myself.' So that this kind of contradiction would give us megalomania, which we may regard as a *sexual over-estimation of the ego* and may thus set beside the over-estimation of the love-object with which we are already familiar."

Thus Freud's theory of paranoia begins with a repressed homosexual wish expressed in the formula, "I (a man) *love him* (a man)," and then goes on to describe the various ways in which this wish can be denied and projected. Freud, of course, was not unaware that the most prominent clinical feature in paranoia was the patient's complaint of social humiliation. He even commented on this:

Paranoia is a disorder in which a sexual aetiology is by no means obvious; on the contrary, the strikingly prominent features in the causation of paranoia, especially among males, are social humiliations and slights. But if we go into the matter only a little more deeply, we shall be able to see that the really operative factor in these social injuries lies in the part played in them by the homosexual components of affective life. So long as the individual is functioning normally and it is consequently impossible to see into the depths of his mental life, there is justification for doubting whether his emotional relations to his neighbours in society have anything to do with sexuality, either actually or genetically. But the development of delusions never fails to unmask these relations and to trace back the social feelings to their roots in a purely sensual erotic wish.[5]

This is a good example of the reasoning made necessary by an inflexible frame of reference incapable of encompassing the empirical facts; rather, the facts must be molded to fit the frame of reference. As I shall attempt to show, social humiliation is the end result of a failure in social adaptation and can be explained in purely adaptational terms without recourse to a sexual instinct.

The Adaptational Psychodynamics of the Pseudohomosexual Conflict

The pseudohomosexual conflict can develop only in those men who fail to meet successfully the societal standards for masculine performance. There are two ways to account for such failures: either the man never learned how to meet these standards; or he learned how, but it does him little good because he suffers from an inhibition of assertion and cannot put his knowledge to effective use. Since I am concerned here only with the latter possibility, it is important to establish from the outset where inhibitions of assertion come from: they originate in childhood from power struggles between the growing child and either his parents or his siblings. These struggles are inevitably perceived unconsciously in symbolic terms of murderous violence in which each of the adversaries seeks to kill the other. Since the forces arrayed against the child are so great that he dare not risk an aggressive move for fear of lethal retaliation, an inhibition of aggression is the logical outcome of such a power struggle. Once an inhibition of aggression is laid down, it is not long before the child symbolically extends his violent conception of aggression to encompass nonhostile assertion as well. The end result in the adult is an inhibition of assertion in all its forms, with or without hostile intent.

The nonassertive male may unconsciously react to his failures in terms of a symbolic equation that sets in motion the pseudohomosexual anxiety. This equation is the following: *I am a failure = I am not a man = I am castrated = I am a woman = I am a homosexual.* In essence, therefore, the pseudohomosexual conflict represents a failure in "masculine" assertion, and each idea in this equation reflects a social value judgment. It follows, then, that this failure in assertion does not exist in social isolation, but is perceived as a competitive defeat by other men. The defeat, in turn, is placed in a dominance-submission context in which the weaker male is castrated by the stronger male and forced to submit to him as a woman. The weaker male attempts to avoid this fate, and to avoid the pseudohomosexual anxiety that goes with it, by resort to one or both of two defensive measures, neither of which is successful.

Motivationally, these measures have to do with strivings for power and dependency. Paradoxically, they serve only to perpetuate the very anxiety they were designed to alleviate. The power-driven male tries to dissipate his weakness in a compensatory fashion through a show of strength, and to this end he is continuously engaged in competition with other men. There is no discrimination about this competition; it is about anything and everything. Unfortunately, his conviction of inadequacy is so strong that he concedes defeat in advance. The result is a chronic pseudohomosexual anxiety. Resort to dependency fares no better. The dependent pseudohomosexual male seeks the magical protection of an omnipotent father-substitute via the equation, *penis = breast*. He aspires to repair his castration through a magical reparative fantasy of oral or anal incorporation of the stronger man's penis, thus making the donor's strength available to him. This maneuver is doomed not only because it is magical and hence cannot succeed in any case, but also because the fantasied act of incorporation is misinterpreted as truly homosexual in its motivation. Thus, as in the case of power, the dependency fantasy intensifies the pseudohomosexual anxiety.

THE POWER MOTIVE.—All these facets of the pseudohomosexual conflict can be easily demonstrated in clinical material. The following sequence of two dreams is an example of the power motive. The patient, the second of three brothers, found himself involved in a competitive transference in which he reproduced his sibling rivalry. The immediate stimulus for the first dream was the patient's hostile preoccupation with the therapist's greater income in contrast to his own:

I was fighting with my older brother. He was much bigger and stronger than me. He threw me on my back and pinned my arms to the ground with his knees. Then he pried open my mouth and forced his penis into it and made me suck it.

The patient found the dream extremely unpleasant and was reluctant to report it. He remembered that as a boy his older brother on several occasions had pinned him to the ground, pried open his mouth, and spat into it, but there had never been anything sexual between them. The patient had experienced no erotic homosexual feelings in the dream, nor, for that matter, at any other time in his life; yet the dream created a concern that he might be a homosexual. Motivationally, however, the dream has nothing to do with sex, but makes use of a homosexual act to symbolize his competitive defeat at the hands of the therapist, represented in the dream as his older brother. The dream, therefore, is a paranoid expression of his competitive hostility couched in terms of oral rape. The patient left the interview in which he reported this dream considerably relieved to find that he was not a homosexual, but he was hardly delighted with the implication of competitive inferiority to the therapist.

That night he had another dream, an exact replica in its action of the first, but this time he did to his younger brother what previously his older brother had done to him. In this dream the therapist was represented by the younger brother, and the patient's hostile impulse came through without projection. Now the score was even; the patient had made a woman out of the therapist, and in so doing had retrieved his lost masculinity.

The hierarchal integration of this patient's relationships with other males is typical of the pseudohomosexual conflict. The integration is on the basis of an old army principle. Simply stated, the principle is the following: There's always a bigger bastard.

In the next example, another patient, a doctor, made use of the same principle, but introduced the added feature of castration. This dream was prompted by a competition with the therapist about professional status:

There were two dogs—that is, either people or dogs. One was big and one was little. The big one was a giant; the little one was a child, a puppy. Both dogs were males. The big dog walked the little dog to the sofa, bent him over and had anal intercourse with him. Then the big dog bent down and bit off the little dog's genitals, clean off, everything.

Here, the dog-eat-dog philosophy inherent in the power struggle was expressed somewhat more literally than in the previous example. The patient awakened with feelings of repulsion and disgust and an anxiety about homosexuality, but without erotic motivation. In his report of the dream, it became clear that the sofa was the analyst's couch, defining the locale of the dream. The patient identified the big dog as the therapist, the puppy as himself. The tremendous disparity in size between the two dogs made him think of father and son. His subsequent associations made it clear that the transference component of the dream derived from his infantile relationship with his father.

One more example will suffice to illustrate the pseudohomosexual elaborations of the power struggle. An illustrator who had had a series of drawings rejected by a desirable magazine, reported the following dream:

The magazine printed one of my drawings, but under another artist's name, and they made the drawing so small you could hardly see it. Then a bull was attacking me. He had me impaled on his horns and was biting my thumb and running around and around with me on his head. I yelled for my cousin to act like a cow so the bull would get interested in him and let me go.

The bull that castrated and anally raped the patient represented his competitors, who had been more successful than he in getting their work published. His cousin, whom he exhorted to act like a cow, was an unskilled laborer, and in comparison with the patient, a complete vocational failure. Thus, vocational success was symbolically equated with masculine strength; vocational failure with feminine weakness. The penalty for failure was not only social humiliation, but also castration, rape, and subjugation as a woman by the victorious male competitors. The patient, of course, did not like such treatment in the least, and so he protested defensively that his cousin, a real failure, was more suited to the feminine role than he was. This dream, therefore, contained all the elements of the symbolic equation previously cited: a vocational failure led to social humiliation and then via the paranoid mechanism was simultaneously expressed in terms of homosexuality, castration, and feminity. The patient produced no homosexual motivation, nor in such a dream would any be expected. The motivation was solely that of power, and the associated anxiety was solely a pseudohomosexual anxiety.

THE DEPENDENCY MOTIVE.—The resort to dependency represents the seeking of magical solutions to the failures in assertion which I have already described. Consider, for example, the following case of a dependent male with a marked inhibition of assertion.† He found it next to impossible to make an independent decision in any activity whatsoever. Instead, he became paralyzed by endless procrastination, and usually ended up by doing nothing. He came to treatment presumably to achieve self-sufficiency, but his unconscious productions pointed to a diametrically opposite motivation. In reality, he sought an omnipotent parent-figure, who would magically take over and run his life for him. This was his sixth attempt at therapy; he had tried five previous psychiatrists, with whom he remained in treatment for varying periods from a few months to as long as two years. In each instance the patient broke off with the complaint that nothing was

† I am indebted for this example to Dr. Julian Barish.

being done for him. Nevertheless, he had not yet given up hope. This he indicated in his opening dream at the end of the second week in his current therapy. The dream not only revealed his magical expectations, but also demonstrated an underlying pseudohomosexual response to his failure in "masculine" assertion:

I was watching a television program of Eisenhower leading a round table discussion. It seemed foreboding. I was scared. A little girl was reprimanded for making too much noise.

The action in the dream was symbolic of the therapeutic procedure. He represented himself as a little girl, the therapist as Eisenhower. The derogatory self-image was a measure of his helplessness in two dimensions: infantilism and femininity; likewise, the identification of the therapist with the President was a measure of the omnipotence with which he had once endowed his father and which he now wished to recapture in the therapist. The patient's sexual adaptation was entirely heterosexual, with no evidence of homosexual desire. However, dependency through the protective love a man is inevitably misinterpreted as homosexuality. It is, therefore, safe to predict that as the therapy continues a pseudohomosexual anxiety will be found attached to the dependency wish and to the deflated image that accompanies it. In the dream he took a rather dim view of the present therapist's ability to render magical aid, and he anticipated only a rebuke for his infantile demands. Needless to say, such an approach to the therapy augured ill for the prognosis, and there was little reason to hope that the sixth psychiatrist would fare any better than the preceding five.

The desire for dependency through the paternal love of a father-substitute is the most superficial form of the dependency fantasy. The same fantasy on a deeper unconscious level is integrated in a more primitive fashion through the equation *breast = penis*. The patient who resorts to this equation attempts to gratify his dependency needs through the oral or anal incorporation of the stronger man's penis. Clinically, the oral route seems to be the more common. A typical example occurred in a patient with an interesting elaboration of a severe inhibition of aggression.‡ He was afraid to learn how to drive, even though he was under constant pressure from his wife to do so. Finally, one day, she lost her temper and tauntingly scoffed that he was not a man. That same night he dreamed that he went to a butcher shop and ate several hunks of meat. He identified the butcher as the therapist. After waking, he felt the meat had been tainted, and he had a bad taste in his mouth. At the same time he experienced feelings of wrong-doing, revulsion, and guilt. In his next therapeutic hour, he remarked that the bad taste made him fear a homosexual implication in the dream. Then he spontaneously associated "penis" to the meat, and suggested that it was up to the therapist to provide what he lacked. Thus the dream had satisfied this demand through a fellatio fantasy in which he orally incorporated the therapist's penis. Equipped in this way, he felt that he could magically go ahead, resolve his inhibition of aggression, learn to drive a car, and so stand up as a man to his wife. The penalty for this fantasy, however, was a pseudohomosexual anxiety—the result of his misinterpretation of the magical device as homosexual, rather than dependent, in its motivational intent. In patients with a more malignant pathology, the fellatio fantasy not infrequently is acted out. Such patients, at times of great anxiety, may seek out men upon whom they

‡ I am indebted for this example to Dr. Herbert Hendin.

perform fellatio, but with no sexual sensation on their own part.

Anal incorporation can be illustrated by the masturbation fantasy of a patient who developed an ambidextrous technique for simultaneous genital and anal masturbation. He manipulated his penis with one hand while he pumped a thermometer in and out of his anus with the other. In the fantasy that accompanied this act, he imagined himself sandwiched between his mother and father as they were having intercourse. The father's penis entered the patient's anus, emerged as the patient's penis, and then penetrated the mother's vagina. The incorporative fantasy here had a mixed heterosexual, homosexual, and pseudohomosexual motivation. The patient not only secured sexual gratification of both varieties, but he also incorporated the father's penis and magically made use of its strength to repair his own weakness, not just in sexual situations, but in nonsexual situations as well. The homosexual motivation was completely latent, for he had never had any homosexual experiences and engaged exclusively in heterosexual relationships. As one would suspect, however, he had an anxiety about being homosexual; but from the motivational breakdown of his fantasy, it is clear that only a part of this anxiety was a true homosexual anxiety; the rest was a pseudohomosexual anxiety. The sexual motivations were primary during masturbation, but on other occasions the pseudohomosexual motivation of dependency took precedence. Nonsexual situations that called for assertion but generated severe anxiety were thus handled by the patient in a characteristic fashion. He would retire to the nearest lavatory, give his anus a few quick strokes with a thermometer, and then go out and try to assert himself. He always carried a spare thermometer with him for just such a contingency. While the use of the thermometer on such occasions might arouse erotic sensation, it was not primarily a sexual act; rather it was a magical attempt to achieve strength through dependency on the father. Here is a case, therefore, where the magical reparative fantasy of anal incorporation of the penis, when symbolically acted out, was at least temporarily successful, but the cost was an accentuation of both the homosexual and pseudohomosexual components of the patient's anxiety. This case is a good example of the motivational complexities of thoughts, feelings, and acts concerned with actual or symbolic homosexuality.

The Psychotic Integration of the Pseudohomosexual Conflict

The various aspects of the pseudohomosexual conflict described above have been nondelusional in their manifestations. Not one of the patients cited suffered from paranoia, although several made use of the paranoid mechanism. At this point one must distinguish between content and form in psychopathological disturbances. The former is concerned with what the conflict is about; the latter is concerned with how the conflict is handled. Content reflects the impact of social institutions upon the patient; form reflects the psychological integration of that content by the patient. It follows, then, that the same conflict can be integrated psychologically by different patients in different ways. Thus, the pseudohomosexual conflict can occur in either a psychotic or a neurotic setting, and, therefore, can have a delusional, as well as a nondelusional, expression. The psychotic integration of this conflict is characteristically found in paranoia with or without the concomitant presence of true latent homosexuality. Such an integration is demonstrated in the clinical vignette that follows. It will come as no surprise, if one keeps in mind the distinction between content and form, to find that the essential features of the pseudo-homosexual conflict, as they have been described, are in no way altered.

The patient, who was 34 years old, married and with two children, was suffering from incipient paranoid schizophrenia. He was a talented, enormously ambitious, and highly successful young executive who had advanced with phenomenal rapidity to a top position as sales manager of a large business organization. His presenting symptomatology was organized around a growing conviction that he was changing into a woman; he came to the psychiatrist through the intervention of an endocrinologist to whom he had applied for injections of male hormone in the hope that they would halt the supposed transformation.

The patient had always had the fear that he was "effeminate," even though objectively he was completely masculine in his physical appearance and in his behavior. However, this fear had never seriously interfered with his capacity to function until the past year, when it had begun to assume delusional proportions.

Strangely enough, the intensification of his anxiety coincided in time with his promotion to sales manager. At first glance, this might seem a paradox; it would be more reasonable for such a success to enhance his masculinity, rather than to undermine it. However, in this case, the unexpected occurred, but not without a hidden logic that will soon be made apparent. The patient was now, by the time he came to treatment, practically convinced that a bodily alteration was in process—that his voice was higher, that his hips were larger, and that he was beginning to walk with a flounce. None of this, of course, was true; but nevertheless, it was what he believed. He was convinced that at the rate things were going it wouldn't be long before his genitals were affected, and then the alteration would be complete. He was terrified at this prospect and repeatedly examined his genitals for signs of shrinkage. As yet, he admitted to no change, but he was convinced the outlook was bleak. He offered a neat explanation for these difficulties: they were all due to excessive masturbation in childhood. As he put it, there were only so many shots in the magazine, and once you used them up, transformation into a woman was inevitable.

The preoccupation with femininity gave rise to a series of related symptoms characteristic of paranoia. Foremost among these were ideas of reference in which he repeatedly misinterpreted the remarks and actions of people around him. He believed they referred to him as effeminate and as a homosexual. To make matters worse, these ideas, almost imperceptibly but quite definitely, were beginning to shade off into delusions of persecution. His potency had always been and remained normal, but there had been a marked lessening of sexual activity since the onset of his illness. This was due not so much to an absence of sexual desire, but rather to his reluctance to engage in intercourse even when the desire was present. This reluctance had its source in his ideas about masturbation—intercourse would further deplete his supply of semen and, hence, it was best avoided. But although abstinence might suit the patient's needs, his wife was starting to complain, and he feared momentarily that she might look for other men. He was gradually becoming more and more suspicious, although he still conceded that her behavior was above reproach. Doubts of this kind, however, are the early precursors of delusions of jealousy.

The patient also confessed to repetitive fantasies in which he performed fellatio, always on the same man—his uncle, a business tycoon of considerable prominence, whom the patient greatly admired and whom he would like to emulate. These were typical pseudohomosexual oral incorporative fantasies. They were unaccompanied by erotic sensation, but the patient misinterpreted them as truly homosexual and offered them as further evidence of his progress toward femininity. In reality, he had never experienced any homosexual activity.

The early history of the patient included the following data:

The patient was a fraternal twin; he and his twin brother were the youngest of twelve siblings, six males and six females. The father had died before the patient was 6 months old. The mother was a decent sort who did her best; but with twelve children, the competition for her attention was fierce. The patient was born into a family of giants. Each of his brothers, including his twin, was over six feet tall, and each of his sisters was five feet eight or taller. Unhappily, the patient himself was only five feet six. The psychological problem this created for him resulted in his embarking on an endless but unsuccessful competitive effort designed to disprove his conviction of inferiority. This effort was doomed to failure from the start, for the simple reason that he could never surmount the disparity in size, no matter how hard he tried, nor how successful were his accomplishments.

Finally the patient had come to attribute his failure to masturbation—a superficial rationalization which served mainly to hide from him where the real problem lay. The heart of the matter was the sibling struggle, first for dependency and then for power, and it was the psychological derivatives of this struggle that were the prime movers in his paranoid breakdown.

The basic psychodynamic pattern climactically emerged at the end of six months of psychotherapy. First, there was a brief period of relative quiescence, manifestly a transference improvement; then, as the unconscious conflict began to approach the surface, the patient's anxiety became more and more intense. There was talk of quitting his job, and with it, of course, the therapy, and retiring in obscurity to a small country town where he would see out his days free from competitive strain running a gasoline station. At it turned out, this was no idle threat. Abruptly one day he resigned from his job, and came to take his leave from the therapy. Fortunately, for the purpose of understanding the pseudohomosexual conflict, he brought with him a dream that laid bare the underlying psychodynamics and explained the precipitate haste with which he made his final decision.

Mother gave me a pint of food, a salad, on a plate. A half a dozen young boys with spears were chasing me. They wanted to take the salad away from me. They wanted it for themselves. I tripped over a rock and the plate dropped into a small pond. The salad stayed on top of the water, but the plate sank. I put my hand into the water to get the plate, but then I couldn't pull my arm out. It was held tight by a lot of worms. The gang of boys cornered me and they started to prod me from behind like savages with their spears. I don't know whether I got out of there alive or not.

This was an obvious sibling rivalry dream in which the patient made use of primitive symbols to express the lethal nature of the original competition for the mother, both as a dependency and as a sexual object. This competition in childhood had first been conceived in the

usual terms of murderous violence and then, later, subjected to a pseudohomosexual elaboration. Consequently,
as an adult, the patient anticipated as retaliation for any
competitive effort not only death, but also the retaliatory
measures that are a part of the pseudohomosexual conflict: castration and oral/anal rape. The dream brings to
light an intermediate step in this man's illness. This step
is commonly referred to as a *success phobia* and defines
the patient's inability to tolerate the successful achievement of ambitious goals because he foresaw the retaliation
from his competitors as inevitable. It is this conflict that
ultimately found expression through the paranoid mechanism; and rather than face it, the patient ran away from
both his job and the therapy. In retrospect, it is a moot
question whether the better choice would have been to
stay and meet the problem head-on. In view of the mal-
ignancy of the patient's pathology, a good case can certainly be made out for the course he took, but that is
another matter which is beyond the scope of this chapter.

The success phobia clarifies an issue that was left hang-
ing; it explains the paradoxical observation that the patient
broke down at the peak of his vocational success. This
was the moment of greatest danger, and to the patient it
represented a delusional materialization of the expected
retaliation. At this instant the delusion of femininity was
established and the overt paranoid psychosis was set in
motion.

An Adaptational Theory of Paranoia

I am now in a position to attempt an adaptational revision of the Freudian theory of paranoia in the male.
This revision is based on the concept of pseudohomosexuality and is equally applicable to nondelusional manifestations of the paranoid mechanism. The material for

such a revision has been organized in Table II under five sequential headings, as follows:

True Motivation.—This is teleologically determined—that is, in terms of the ultimate adaptational goal.

Symbolic Distortion.—This describes how the meaning of the true motivation is altered in the unconscious mind.

Apparent (False) Motivation.—This is the motivation as it is perceived by the patient after the true motivation has undergone symbolic distortion.

Projected Idea.—This is the paranoid defense against the apparent motivation.

Anxiety.—This defines the related anxiety. The table makes clear the distinction between the homosexual anxiety and the pseudohomosexual anxiety: the former stems from a true homosexual motivation; the latter stems from an apparent (false) homosexual motivation symbolically derived from the unconscious distortion of the true motivations of power and dependency.

In demonstrating by means of this table the various motivations that can give rise to the paranoid mechanism, I have not totally discarded the original Freudian conclusion that true homosexuality is always the basis of paranoia, but have modified and incorporated it in the revision. The table explains the clinical discrepancy in the Freudian theory previously noted that paranoid patients have repeatedly been studied who showed no evidence of true homosexuality. The table makes clear that the homosexual motivation is in no way exclusive; in fact, I would go so far as to suggest that it is the pure power (aggression) motivation without any pseudohomosexual elaboration that is the constant feature in paranoid phenomena, and that the essential related anxiety is, therefore, a survival anxiety. In contrast, the pseudohomosexual components of both the power and the dependency motivations, the true homosexual motivation, and the survival

TABLE II

True Motivation	Symbolic Distortion	Apparent (False) Motivation	Projected Idea	Anxiety
HOMOSEXUAL: I want homosexual gratification from him.	None.	None.	He wants homosexual gratification from me.	HOMOSEXUAL
POWER (AGGRESSION): I want to subject him to competitive defeat.	I want to kill him.	POWER (AGGRESSION = MURDER): I want to kill him.	He wants to kill me.	SURVIVAL
	I want to castrate him and make a woman (homosexual) of him.	POWER (AGGRESSION = CASTRATION): I want to castrate him and make a woman (homosexual) of him.	He wants to castrate me and make a woman (homosexual) of me.	CASTRATION and PSEUDOHOMOSEXUAL
	I want to subjugate him as a woman (homosexual) = I want to subject him to oral/anal rape.	HOMOSEXUAL: I want oral/anal homosexual gratification from him.	He wants oral/anal homosexual gratification from me = He wants to subject me to oral/anal rape.	PSEUDOHOMOSEXUAL
DEPENDENCY: I want to be dependent on him = I want him to love me (nonsexually).	I want him to love me (sexually).	HOMOSEXUAL: I want homosexual gratification from him.	He wants homosexual gratification from me.	PSEUDOHOMOSEXUAL
	I want to incorporate his penis orally/anally.	HOMOSEXUAL: I want oral/anal homosexual gratification from him.	He wants oral/anal homosexual gratification from me = He wants to subject me to oral/anal rape.	PSEUDOHOMOSEXUAL
DEPENDENCY + FRUSTRATION → AGGRESSION = I hate him because he won't let me be dependent on	I want to kill him.	AGGRESSION = MURDER: I want to kill him.	He wants to kill me.	SURVIVAL

component of the dependency motivation are all variables that can be present or absent, as the case may be. Furthermore, in my clinical experience, the pseudohomosexual motivations occur with far greater frequency than does the homosexual one. This is especially true in nondelusional manifestations of the paranoid mechanism, where true homosexuality appears to be relatively rare. The table also shows that the hatred that stems from dependency-frustration can ultimately be experienced as a projected attack by the dependency-object. The most simple delusional representation of this attack is murder. A more complicated form, the delusion of being poisoned, is integrated through the equation: *penis = breast = food*. Dependency-gratification is equated with good food; dependency-frustration with bad food. Poison then symbolically derives from the latter. Here, the patient's reasoning is either black or white. If the dependency-object isn't for him, then he's against him; if he doesn't intend to feed him, then he intends to poison him. The nature of paranoia does not permit of a neutral position. In those cases where the dependency-object is a woman, the equation is reduced to its nucleus: *breast = food*. There are many other interesting elaborations of this equation, but their description is not in the main stream of this chapter, and, therefore, must be omitted.

Alternative pseudohomosexual explanations for each of the four principal forms of paranoia cited by Freud now became self-evident:

(1) *The delusion of persecution* is amply explained in the table.

(2) *Erotomania* is a compensatory attempt to repair a pseudohomosexual failure in "masculine" assertion by resort to the sexual conquest of women.

(3) *The delusion of jealousy* expresses the conviction of

the pseudohomosexual male that he cannot hold a woman against the competition of stronger men. He may then have pseudohomosexual fantasies involving his more powerful rivals, and these fantasies will be misinterpreted by him as truly homosexual.

(4) *Megalomania* is a compensatory attempt at ego-inflation where the self-esteem is woefully weak. Pseudohomosexuality plays a role in megalomania to whatever extent it contributes to such low self-esteem. The same, for that matter, can also be said of homosexuality, and, adaptationally, that is the only connection between homosexuality and megalomania. Restating this adaptational premise in libidinal terms, in my opinion, adds nothing to one's understanding of it. For this reason, the energic explanation of megalomania offered by Freud seems to me purely a flight of fancy made necessary by his adherence to the libido theory.

The adaptational theory of the paranoid mechanism and paranoi described in this chapter, unlike the classical Freudian theory, agrees completely with the observable clinical facts. The revision was made possible by altering the frame of reference within which the paranoid phenomena were examined. The adaptational formulation that has emerged is not merely of academic interest, but can have great practical significance for dynamic psychotherapy. Such a therapy cannot succeed unless it is based on an accurate motivational breakdown of the patient's behavior. The proposed theory provides this breakdown for the male patient with paranoid manifestations.

CHAPTER 4

Masculine Aspirations in Women

An Adaptational Analysis

Introduction

MASCULINE aspirations are frequently expressed by women patients during the course of a dynamic psychotherapy. The interpretation placed upon these aspirations by the therapist can be of vital importance to the ultimate outcome of the therapy. The purpose of this chapter is to subject the wish to be a man to an adaptational analysis and to demonstrate the adaptational psychodynamics that lie behind that wish. The chapter will provide a limited but cohesive theoretical framework within which any adaptational variant of the wish can be fitted, understood, and treated.

The term adaptation refers to the behavioral maneuvers by means of which the person *adapts* to his social environment as he seeks to insure his survival and gratify his needs. An adaptational analysis of masculine aspirations in women, therefore, must begin with an examination of the social realities to which women in American society must adapt. The emancipation of women that began with the industrial revolution has been especially rapid in America since the turn of the century. The social position of women has been in a continuous state of change, and the society has not always been able to supply specific social directives for "masculine" or "feminine" behavior. Nevertheless, as of today, the society is still a male-oriented society in which the position of women is devalued. The social order is so arranged that status accrues to men solely by virtue of the fact that they are men. The polarities of masculinity and feminity are identified respectively with positive and negative value judgments. Masculinity represents strength, dominance, superiority; femininity represents weakness, submissiveness, inferiority. The former is equated with success; the latter with failure. It is true that these values are cultural stereotypes that express primarily the historical prejudices of the men in the culture. However, it would be safe to say that men and women alike make use of them in appraising each other's behavior.

The adaptational responses of women to these institutional pressures in many ways are similar to the responses of members of the minority group in a caste system.[1] Many women—although by no means all—consciously reject this prejudicial picture of themselves, but it is doubtful that few, if any, completely escape its deleterious effects on an unconscious level. Women must struggle against deflation of the self-esteem and the self-contempt that goes with it. There is a measure of resentment against men, and there are some wishful fantasies of exchanging places with them. These are normal responses to the social institutions that provoke them, and they do not seriously interfere with the acceptance of womanhood and of woman's sociobiological role.

The normal aspiration to be a man that has just been described may undergo a neurotic integration. This occurs through a symbolic extension in which the unconscious symbol par excellence of masculine superiority becomes the penis. Conversely, the symbol of feminine inferiority becomes the absence of a penis—that is, a castration. These unconscious symbolic extractions from the social institutions are common occurrences among patients in dynamic psychotherapy. They are used by male patients as well as by female, and every therapist is regularly a witness to them. They form the basis for a process of magical repair by means of which the neurotic woman in fantasy gains access to masculine traits and the boons that go with them. This process consists of the magical acquisition of the penis. The manner of its acquisition is derived from the woman's early developmental responses to sexual institutions.

Attitudes toward sex in this society are still predominantly punitive. The growing child unconsciously believes that sexual transgressions will be punished by withdrawal of parental love, loss of dependency, castration, and death. Clinical studies demonstrate that the little girl frequently invokes the castration fantasy to explain the anatomical difference between herself and the little boy. She believes that she once had a penis and that it was cut off as a punishment for her sexual misdeeds. The fantasy is usually integrated through the oedipus complex, in which the punitive figure is the parent of the same sex, and for this reason the little girl commonly blames her mother for the lack of penis. The castration-anxiety may give rise to magical reparative fantasies through which a new penis is acquired. The original purpose of these fantasies in the child is to reinstate the bodily integrity and thus to allay the castration-anxiety. Once the fantasies are laid down, the woman thereafter may resort to them whenever such an anxiety is aroused. These fantasies take various forms. The woman may simply appeal to her mother to return the penis to her; or she may seek to borrow the penis from her father or from a fantasied phallic mother, or from their symbolic surrogates. More complicated forms of the fantasy are based on the equations, *baby = penis* or *feces = penis*, through which the woman regenerates a penis within her own body. These are all harmless wishful fantasies. They do not solve the problem of castration, but neither do they aggravate it. More often, however, the repair is conceived as an act of destruction in which the penis is taken by force from an unwilling male donor, originally the father, later a father-substitute. Most frequently the penis is incorporated orally or vaginally. Sometimes it is torn manually from the donor and in some magical fashion attached to the perineum of the recipient. Rarely, it is incorporated *per anum*. In all of these cases the wish not only fails to alleviate the castration-anxiety, but even adds to it because it carries with it the threat of violent retaliation. To make matters worse, this threat, as I shall show, can create serious disturbances in the woman's relationships with men in both the sexual and nonsexual areas of behavior.

It is common knowledge that castration-anxiety in the adult woman occurs in those sexual situations that revive the infantile expectation of punishment for sexual transgression. It is not so well known that the same anxiety can be aroused by an adaptative failure in nonsexual assertion. Such failures may set in motion a symbolic equation that recapitulates the infantile castration. The equation is the following: *I am a failure = I am not a man = I am a woman = I am castrated.* The reparative fantasies that follow in the wake of this equation are exactly the same as those originally used by the little girl to undo her castration. Their purpose now, however, goes far beyond mere anatomical repair. The woman does not want a penis just for its own sake, but conceives of it as a magical instrument that will improve her performance. She hopes through its incorporation to acquire masculine adaptive capacities, reverse her failure, and guarantee a successful adaptation. Thus, in an adaptational context, the neurotic aspiration to be a man emerges as a wish for magical aid. This wish is integrated behaviorally through the motivations of dependency and power.

The Dependency Motivation

What is dependency?[2] It is a technique of adaptation through reliance on another person. It is based on a conviction of helplessness and is normal in infancy, but infantile dependency in the adult is a confession of adaptive failure. The developmental prototype for the dependency relationship is the relationship between the child and the mother. It is this relationship that the dependent adult seeks to reestablish. To this end he solicits support, help, protection. In extreme instances he wants another person to take over all responsibility for his welfare just as his mother did when he was a child. These are the conscious expressions of the wish to be dependent.

Unconsciously, the wish is expressed in terms of being fed, an act that symbolizes the incorporation of the maternal breast. In this way the dependent person hopes to recapture the infantile state in which his every need was gratified by the all-powerful mother. The breast-fantasy is the most direct route to dependency-gratification. There is, however, an alternative route via the equation, *penis = breast*. There are two ways in which this equation can be used. The first conceives of the father's penis as a feeding organ similar to the mother's breast. The reparative fantasy is then one of sucking the penis in which the semen is equated with milk. No incorporation of the penis need be involved, and the woman who makes use of this fantasy may do so without any desire to be a man. The second way involves the incorporation of the penis and the subsequent alteration of the woman into a man. It is this fantasy that forms the basis for masculine aspirations in the dependent woman. The fantasy is made possible by the magical properties symbolically assigned to the male genital in the culture.

The interactions between the dependent woman and her social environment that generate the wish to be a man are best demonstrated through clinical material. The first example is that of a dependent young woman, who lacked confidence in herself, and, in spite of repeated efforts, was unable to find a job. She always made such a poor impression on the prospective employer that inevitably she was turned away. Her discouragement provoked a revealing series of three dreams. The first dream was the following:

She was lying in bed with a broken leg in a dingy apartment in a red-light district. She went out to a grocery store to buy some food. The proprietress was a black-haired, middle-aged woman, who resembled her mother. She refused to wait on the patient and instead looked menacingly at her. The patient became frightened and ran out of the store. As she crossed the street, the same woman, driving a huge bus, tried to run over her.

This dream demonstrates the symbolic relationship between adaptive failure and castration. The castration is then characteristically explained as a punishment for sexual misbehavior. The punitive agent is the mother, who not only has castrated the patient, but also refuses to feed her and then tries to kill her. In her associations the patient insisted that if only she were a man she would have no trouble in either finding or holding a job. This was a blatant rationalization in view of the fact that every employer who had rejected her had advertised for a woman applicant to fill the vacant position. This sort of rationalization is typical of the dependent woman. She puts the blame for her failure on the accident of gender, and the lack of a penis, instead of facing the responsibility for learning to do better. The therapist pointed this out to her, but she did not accept it, and the next night in another dream again blamed the mother for her helplessness. She dreamed that the mother was arrested for the murder of a little boy, whom she identified with herself. A trial was held and the mother was sentenced to hang for the crime. The patient did not feel the least bit sorry. Instead, she awoke quite pleased with the dream. Now the mother had been punished for the castration that had transformed her from a supposedly capable male into a helpless female. The dream made her happy, but it hardly solved her problem. She still remained without a job. Her solution was a magical one, and it emerged in the next dream:

She was an inmate of an orphan asylum in which her mother was the headmistress, but she was not her mother's child. She was not able to get enough food from her mother, so she stole a goldfish and swallowed it. The fish belonged to a tall, thin man. He discovered it was gone and was furious. The mother told him the patient had stolen his fish. He demanded she give it back, but she refused and ran away. He chased after her.

She identified the tall, thin man as her father, and the goldfish represented his penis. The dream is ambivalently based on the good-mother–bad-mother concept. She sees her mother as the bad mother and, therefore, represents herself as an orphan. She is convinced that the mother will not feed her, and so she attempts to solve the problem of dependency in another way, through the equation, *penis = breast*. She takes by stealth that which is denied her, but then she is left with a fear of retaliation. The dream demonstrates the oral incorporation of a penis. In this manner, the patient magically repairs her castration and the donor's masculine properties become available to her.

The next example demonstrates the same ideation, but the appeal for a penis is made to the mother and completely by-passes the father. The patient in this instance was a dependent homosexual woman of 26 who was living in a mother-daughter type of homosexual relationship with an older woman. She entered therapy because she was dissatisfied with her existence and saw no future in it. She wanted to break off with her paramour in order to go out with men, but the prospect of being on her own frightened her so much that she had been unable to make the break. In the course of the therapy she was eventually confronted with the necessity of taking the decisive step of leaving the protection of the older woman. She daily proclaimed to the therapist her readiness to do so, but the days passed, and she failed to make the move. Instead, in her dreams, she proposed a series of alternatives, each of which permitted her to retain a dependent adaptation.

First, she dreamed that she left the older woman, but only to be adopted by a wealthy, widowed uncle, who, in reality, had considerable renown as an amateur chef and whose larder was stocked with fine imported foods. In the dream she feasted on the many delicacies he prepared, and she felt well-fed, safe, and happy. The therapist pointed out that she had simply exchanged a maternal object for a paternal object, and that the underlying need for dependency had been left intact.

The patient then reported another dream. Once again she left the older woman, but this time she married the therapist, who loved her very dearly and provided for her every need. The therapist agreed that this was an improvement over the previous dream, and was a move in the desired heterosexual direction, but it still did not solve her basic problem—that of dependency. It was this problem that stood in her way, and she would never leave the older woman until she faced it.

That night the patient dreamed that she took her pet cat, a spayed male, to her childhood home and asked her mother to exchange it for an intact male with a penis. She identified herself with the castrated male cat, and then in her associations she explained that going into the world as an independent person was a masculine pursuit, and if she could be changed into a man she was sure she could accomplish it. It was up to her mother, who was originally responsible for her castration, to replace the missing penis. The therapist interpreted this wish as still another magical solution, just like the first two, and, as such, it would work no better. She would have to learn to be independent as a woman. The penis had nothing to do with it. At any rate, it was not possible to get one and, therefore, she really had no choice.

The patient felt trapped by this challenge, and in her

next dream she saw herself with the therapist in his office, but she was suddenly struck deaf and she heard nothing that he said. In this way she hoped to ward off the therapy and hold on to her neurotic dependency. The therapist commented simply that this wouldn't work either.

The patient thereupon dreamed that the therapist was murdered. This was her last defensive maneuver. She finally got down to business, and in the next few weeks moved away from the older woman into an apartment of her own.

Two other reparative fantasies involving the acquisition of a penis occur in dependent women with sufficient frequency to warrant their mention. One of these occurs in dependent women who had male siblings that were favored by their parents, or whose parents wanted a boy. A failure in adaptation in such women fosters the wish to be a boy on the grounds that it would better insure the gratification of dependency needs from parents or parental substitutes. The other fantasy used by dependent women is somewhat more complicated. Some of these women want a penis so that they can displace their fathers, marry their mothers, and have sexual intercourse with them. The motivation in this fantasy is not sexual; rather the patient makes use of the sexual act as an instrument to further her dependency policy. She is not concerned with sexual pleasure for herself, but wants only to give such pleasure to her mother, in return for which she hopes to be repaid with the desired protection and support.

The Power Motivation

Some women, instead of resorting to dependency, attempt to repair feelings of weakness, inadequacy, and inferiority through compensatory strivings for power. These women find dependency abhorrent because it is demeaning to their self-esteem. They are engaged in a constant struggle against an underlying wish to be dependent, which, in the end, they reject. These are the women popularly known as "castrating females." They compensate for their supposed weakness through masculine-dramatization—that is, by an exaggeration of the so-called "masculine" traits. Such women are hard-hitting, extremely competitive, and overly aggressive, particularly with men, and seek always to be in a dominant position. They tend to marry submissive men, who permit them to act out the fantasy of being the husband instead of the wife. This type of woman unconsciously denies the absence of a penis; instead she believes that she has one, and this fantasy enables her to feel the competitive equal of any man, or even the better of the two.

The self-image of the power-driven woman, therefore, differs from the self-image of the dependent woman. The former sees herself as a "phallic" woman; the latter sees herself as a castrated man. This difference in the self-image makes the power-driven woman especially prone to a castration-anxiety. Any threat to the fantasied phallus may generate such an anxiety and lead to a sudden collapse of the adaptive capacity. The threat may consist of an actual failure in adaptation, such as the loss of a job or a competitive defeat; or there need be no actual failure at all, but nevertheless a symbolic perception of the life situation as a castration. The latter category includes insults to the integrity of the body, such as operations and injuries, or changes in the sociobiological role, such as marriage, pregnancy, or childbirth. The end result, however, is exactly the same, whether the failure is real or imagined, and the woman is left with a conviction of helplessness. A power-driven woman who finds herself in this situation generally attempts first to retrieve the penis in order to reinstate the original power position. Her first thought is of self-sufficiency. Should this attempt fail, she may fall back on the only other magical solution available to her, that of dependency. Thus, the two motivations, power and dependency, can be considered opposite sides of the same coin.

The next example demonstrates the disastrous effects of an imagined power-failure incident to a change in sociobiological status. The patient was a very successful, power-driven, professional woman, characteristically aggressive and domineering, who developed a chronic postpartum depression after the birth of her first child. The depression was of only mild severity, and did not seriously interfere with her capacity to work, but it was accompanied by ancillary manifestations that disrupted her relationships both with her child and with her husband. She showed no interest in the child from the moment he was born. She turned the infant over to a housekeeper-nurse as soon as she got him home, and then proceeded completely to ignore him. At the same time she withdrew emotionally from the husband, became unpleasantly irritable, and except on rare occasions, refused to have sexual intercourse with him. Finally, after many months, the husband got fed up and insisted she seek psychiatric help. At first, she protested and would not go, but when he threatened dissolution of the marriage, she gave in and entered a psychoanalytic therapy.

It quickly emerged through a series of typical castration dreams that she had responded to motherhood as though it were a symbolic castration. It had undermined the illusion that she possessed a penis and had confronted her with the inescapable fact that she was a woman. This

to her meant that she was deficient in adaptive equipment and no longer capable of effective performance.
Her dreams were, therefore, dreams of mutilation and of
impaired function. Thus, for example, she dreamed she
had to compete against men in a swimming race, but lost
out to them because her leg was crippled; or again, she
dreamed repeatedly of damaged cars, many of them
blood-spattered, in which parts of the engine were missing, or the engine would not start. Her opening dreams
were monotonous in their regularity, and almost all re-
volved around this single theme of castration and adaptive failure.

The most direct symptomatic expression of her plight
was the depression. It indicated that she had lost confidence in her ability to recoup through phallic power
and had begun instead to turn toward the maternal
breast. The switch to a dependency solution, however,
was not yet complete. This could be inferred from her
other symptoms—the rejection of her roles as wife and
mother, by means of which she denied her femininity
and tenuously held on to the fantasy that she was a man.
She acted out this masculine fantasy in still another way
through an additional symptom that she could not bring
herself to mention to the therapist until long after the
treatment had started. This symptom began right after
the birth of the child and consisted of a change in urinary
habit. She had previously always urinated sitting down,
in the manner customary for women, but now she began
to urinate exclusively in the standing position, just like
a man, except that she straddled the toilet bowl with her
legs, instead of standing in front of it.

It was not long before the patient became involved in
an erotic transference. This set off an Oedipal trend that
finally terminated in a nightmare in which she reenacted

the infantile castration by her mother. The nightmare was the following:

A sadistic old crone was torturing a group of young women. She removed their eyes with a knife and left a watery space where each eye had been. Then she slashed their mouths from ear to ear. One by one she disfigured them. The patient was the only one not disfigured. Then the old woman began to threaten her. The patient shrieked, "Don't do it to me!" She woke up in terror.

This dream was the clincher. It had an emotional impact far greater than all the others. It was as though for the first time the patient really grasped that she had no penis. This insight unleashed a castration-anxiety that could perhaps better be called a panic, and at the same time plunged the patient into a severe agitated depression. She now went into an adaptive paralysis that lasted for several months. She behaved as though she were in a daze. At home she became more uncommunicative than ever. She did manage to go to work each day, but it was only a holding operation, and she got very little done. She merely went through the motions. She insisted that she was helpless and could not function without the penis. Now that the fantasy was gone she felt revealed as a fraud. She, herself, had never really done anything. It had all been done magically through the fantasy, and she could take no credit for it. Not only were her past accomplishments reduced to naught, but she could never accomplish anything again. The situation was hopeless. She should never have come into therapy. At least, then, her fantasy would have remained intact and she could have maintained her previous adaptation. It might not have been the most satisfactory, but it had certainly been better than nothing. The therapist tried to support the patient through this crisis. He pointed out again and again that nothing in reality had changed. She was still the same person. She still had the same resources. The many things she had done before with the help of the fantasy she could continue to do now without it. But the patient would have none of this. Instead, she tried desperately through her dreams to retrieve the fantasied penis.

I have selected four dreams, typical of this period in the therapy, to illustrate the different mechanisms used by the patient to incorporate the penis. The particular dreams that follow are self-evident in their symbolism, and it is precisely for that reason that I have selected them. In the first dream the patient made use of oral incorporation:

She went to a parking lot to get her car, but it was gone. There was an empty space where her car had been. She began to search for it. She saw a car all smashed up and thought at first that it was hers, but then it turned out not to be. She looked and looked, but couldn't find it. Suddenly, she felt something stuck in her throat. It was some kind of food, but it felt like rubber. She tried to swallow it, but it wouldn't go down. She reached in with a finger and pulled it out. Then she saw that it was a condom.

The patient was revolted by the dream. She awoke with a mild globus hystericus that lasted most of the day. At first, in her associations, she confused the intent to incorporate the penis with the sexual act of fellatio, and felt that that was the reason she had been so revolted by the dream and why she had suffered the globus symptom. The motivational context in which the dream occurred, however, had nothing to do with sex, and, in such cases, the therapist must take care not to com-

pound the confusion. The dream was therefore interpreted as a reparative attempt to undo the castration.

In the second dream the patient made use of a vaginal
incorporation that aroused a fear of retaliation:

There was a watery space in her garden where nothing
would grow. The man next door had a rose bed with long-
stemmed roses. She was sure one of them would grow in
her empty space. She sneaked into his yard and sliced off
a rose stem with a razor. She stuck it into the space in her
garden, but it, too, failed to grow. She asked her husband
to replant it, but deeper; maybe then it would grow. She
noticed a policeman watching from across the street. Her
husband said, "He's going to arrest you. This rose isn't
your property. You better put it back where you got it
from."

The patient related the dream to her husband's request for intercourse the night before. She had refused
the request and he had become very annoyed. As a matter of fact, she had not had intercourse for three months,
ever since the onset of the acute castration-anxiety. At
the time of the present dream, however, her withdrawal
from intercourse seemed to be related not only to the
fear of maternal castration, but also to the fear of retaliation from the husband because of her desire to remove
his penis and attach it to herself. The underlying fantasy
here is a vagina dentata fantasy, which is a common
cause of sexual inhibition in women patients with masculine aspirations.

In the third dream she attempted to steal the penis
from her father:

It was a long time ago when she was a child, although in
the dream she appeared as an adult. She was in her father's
room. She stole some money from his pants and stuffed
it into a condom. In her haste, she dropped the condom and

it rolled under the bed. She got down on her hands and knees and felt for it. She found it, but her hands got dirty. A policeman chased her. She feared the dirty hands would give her away.

The money stuffed in the condom attested to the adaptive value she placed upon the penis. The dirty hands represented her guilt for having stolen it. Here, again, as in the previous dream, the threat of retaliation from the male donor provided a new source for anxiety.

In the fourth dream she appealed for a penis to a "phallic" mother:

She was pregnant and almost at term. She was working on her car. It had been in a smash-up and was covered with blood. Her membranes broke and she began to go into labor. She began to bleed profusely and was afraid she was going to die. She ran into the house where she lived as a child and begged her mother to do something. The mother stuck an enema nozzle into her vagina. Her husband saw her and said, "What's the matter? Why is that enema stuck inside of you? I'll take it out." She screamed, "No! No! Leave it there."

Her associations dealt with the frequent enemas her mother had given her as a child. The infantile fantasy, therefore, was one of anal incorporation, but in the dream it was transformed and the penis was incorporated vaginally.

Gradually, as each reparative fantasy was analyzed, interpreted, and cut off, the patient's agitation began to burn itself out, but her depression became deeper and deeper. This was taken as a sign that unconsciously she had finally placed her major reliance on the breast and the dependency motivation had become primary. This conclusion was very quickly confirmed through an accident of fate that coincidentally occurred at this time.

Her mother suddenly suffered a mild stroke, and there was some discussion among the relatives of sending her to live with the patient. The thought of taking care of the mother was unbearable to the patient, and not only made her even more depressed, but also sent her into a renewed panic. The possibility that the mother would live with her prompted two dreams that form a complementary pair:

(1) She was writhing in agony because both her breasts were torn off. They had been eaten by her mother and by her child.

(2) Her sister came to visit her. She tore off the sister's clothes and began to chew off the sister's breasts.

These dreams reveal the archaic fantasies that underlie the depressive reaction. Object relationships are established on the basis of who eats whom. The patient conceived of dependency as a cannibalistic act in which the breasts of the dependency object were eaten by the dependent subject, and in this act the donor was destroyed. The patient became additionally depressed because her mother was helpless and, therefore, the patient could no longer be dependent on her—that is, eat the mother's breast. The patient went into a panic because the helpless mother now wanted to be dependent on her—that is, eat the patient's breast. The patient then cast about for another dependency object, settled on her sister as a substitute for the mother, and so dreamed that she ate the sister's breasts. The first dream also revealed a previously hidden reason for her rejection of her child. She refused to let the child be dependent on her, at least partially out of the fear of being eaten.

These two dreams marked a turning point in the analysis. The psychodynamic reconstruction of the central conflict was completed by their interpretation. This made it possible for the patient to begin to act in accordance with reality. At this writing she is still in therapy and is learning—painfully, to be sure—that it is possible for her to take care of herself, perform successfully, and meet her obligations to others without recourse either to the penis or to the breast.

So far, in the discussion of the power motivation, I have dealt mainly with the effects of an imagined power-failure. I should like now to focus on the competitive aspects of this motivation. The vocational, social, and marital areas of behavior provide many opportunities for power struggles between men and women. These struggles are unconsciously perceived in terms of murderous violence and, in addition, are frequently placed in a masculine-feminine context; that is, dominance is symbolized by masculinity, submission by femininity. This is just as true in struggles between men and women as in those between men only, and women who win out in such struggles may, therefore, emerge with the conviction unshaken that they are really "phallic" women. The fantasied fears of retaliation follow logically from these symbolic extensions of the power struggle and consist in both sexes not only of death, but also of the castration of the loser by the victor. It does not matter that the woman in reality has no penis, since in fantasy she believes that she has, and, as I have already shown, castration-anxiety can arise from a threat to an imaginary penis just as well as from a threat to a real penis. The male may also have a retaliatory fear of pseudohomosexual[3] submission to a victorious "phallic" woman. The corollary to this fear in the female is a fear of violent destruction by the man's penis in heterosexual intercourse.

The following episode, which occurred during the psy-

choanalysis of a successful young businesswoman, demonstrates these various features of the power struggle
between men and women. The patient was the only
woman among the executives of a firm. She had got
where she was through sheer ability and hard work and
in spite of the prejudices of the firm against women on
the executive level. One day, she was tipped off by a
friend that a vacancy had occurred higher up, and that
she and a male rival were under consideration for the
promotion. She very much wanted the new job, and
doubled her efforts on the old one to impress her superiors that she deserved it, but she was convinced that
it would go to the man simply because she was a woman.
She spent many therapeutic hours vehemently denounc-
ing the firm, its attitude toward women, and the cultural
institutions that made these attitudes possible. Her rage
was accompanied by considerable anxiety that mounted
in its intensity as the day of decision approached. The
unconscious roots of this anxiety were graphically revealed in a chronological sequence of three dreams. The
first of these was the following:

She was engaged in a battle with some men. She was hack-
ing at them with a hatchet. It seemed that the only way to
destroy them was to hack off their legs, but she was having
a great deal of difficulty because no sooner did she remove
a leg than two others grew in its place. The legs then kept
multiplying, the two became four, the four became eight,
and so on. They multiplied much faster than she could cut
them off. She was surrounded by legs and could see no
escape. She awoke in a state of terror.

Here, the rivalry is represented in a typical fashion
as warfare, and, to win, she must kill the male by cut-
ting off his source of "masculine" power, the penis. Her

immediate association was to the labors of Hercules and his battle with the Hydra, the serpent that had nine heads, any of which, when cut off, was succeeded by two others. This, she remarked, was exactly the way she felt about her competitive struggles with men, but, unlike Hercules, she could look forward only to defeat. Her glum outlook found expression in the next dream. It was a thinly disguised castration dream, and it anticipated the retaliatory loss of her fantasied penis:

A small mole on her upper lip suddenly grew to a huge size. She knew it would have to be removed. An enormous incision would be required because it was so large. This upset her a great deal because the operation would disfigure her mouth.

However, things did not work out as she had anticipated; when the company finally made its announcement, it was she who got the promotion, not the man. She was of course elated, but at the same time somewhat guilty, and her fears of retaliation, instead of disappearing, were quickly displaced to another area of behavior. Two weeks later she informed the therapist that ever since her promotion she had been unable to have sexual intercourse with her husband. The very next time they tried, which was on the day after the good news, and every time thereafter, she immediately experienced a vaginismus that was so severe that her husband could not insert even a finger into the vagina, let alone his penis. She had never had any previous difficulties of this kind. The motivational anxiety that lay behind this symptom emerged very shortly in the next dream:

She was being chased by a man, who was trying to kill her. To escape she had to go through an arena. This turned out to be a bull ring in which a bullfight was going on. The bull tried to gore her. She managed to escape by leaping over a fence.

The night of the dream she had attempted intercourse with her husband, but, as usual, her vaginal sphincter clamped down and the act could not be consummated. This incident was apparently the stimulus that provoked the dream. She identified the man who tried to kill her as the rival she had defeated, and the bull, she thought, represented her husband, who had always been interested in bullfights. The dream demonstrates the inhibitory action that a power struggle with a man may have upon the sexual behavior of a power-driven woman. The sexual relationship is placed in the same context as the power struggle itself, and intercourse is then conceived of as an act of destructive violence in which the woman submits to the domination of the man. Thus, rendered helpless, the woman is exposed to the same retaliations of death and castration that originally, in the power struggle, she had tried to mete out to her male antagonist. In this case, the patient triumphed vocationally, but she displaced the fear of retaliation from her vocational rival to her sexual partner—her husband—and now she feared destruction from the husband in the sexual act. The destructive weapon was the penis, and, therefore, to defend herself she took refuge in a symptom that sealed off the vagina to its entry. The symptom lasted for six weeks and then gradually disappeared as she gained insight into its meaning.

Masculine Aspirations, Pseudohomosexual Anxiety, and Homosexuality

The conflict engendered by masculine aspirations in neurotic women is analogous to the pseudohomosexual conflict in men, since both stem from the motivations of dependency and power. In the man, however, the conflict terminates in an anxiety about being homosexual, while in the woman it usually does not. The reasons for this difference require elucidation. In the man, the wish for dependency, as well as a defeat in a power struggle, may lead to a feminine identification, which may then through symbolic extension be equated with homosexuality. The end result of this symbolic equation is a pseudohomosexual anxiety. This is an anxiety that is derived from the motivations of dependency and power, but is misinterpreted by the patient as homosexual in its intent. In the woman, the same motivations, as I have shown in this chapter, may lead to the desire to be a man, and hence to a masculine identification, but only rarely do they create an anxiety about being homosexual.

How does it happen that feminine identification in the male almost always generates a pseudohomosexual anxiety, whereas masculine identification in the female almost always fails to do so? The answer is not difficult to find. It lies in the social institutions previously described that assign a positive value to masculinity and a negative value to femininity. These judgments make it much harder for a man to accept a homosexual label than for a woman to do so, because in the man it connotes femininity, which has a low status value, while in the woman it connotes masculinity, which has a high status value. Thus, for status reasons, the male rejects his feminine identification and becomes anxious about the homosexuality it symbolizes; the female, on the other hand, readily accepts her masculine identification, since she aspires to be a man, and, therefore, has little reason to be anxious about the homosexuality that is symbolically associated with it.

Masculine aspirations are intimately related to homosexuality in women along the same lines that the pseudohomosexual conflict is related to homosexuality in men. In both cases, the homosexual motivation is primary, but the motivations of dependency and power, by their relative weights, determine the configuration of the homosexual relationship. Thus, among homosexual women, the power motivation will lead to masculine-dramatization, and the woman will play the role of the husband in a husband-wife type of homosexual relationship, or the role of the "phallic" mother in a mother-daughter type of homosexual relationship. It is this dramatization that results in the "masculine" woman commonly known in homosexual circles as the "bull dike." Similarly, a homosexual woman motivated also by dependency will gravitate to the wife or to the daughter role. These are the two extremes; there can be all gradations in between, including relationships based on equality. In such cases, the union is joined primarily for purposes of reciprocal homosexual gratification, and the motivations of dependency or power are less prominent.

The adaptational analysis of masculine aspirations in women presented in this chapter has been especially designed for practical application in the conduct of adaptational psychotherapy. The theory and technique of this type of psychotherapy, and its difference from classical psychoanalysis, has been described at some length elsewhere.[4] The focal point in such a therapy is at all times the patient's adaptation to his social environment. The therapist is primarily concerned with the failures in this adaptation, how they have arisen, and how they can be corrected. He tracks down their developmental origins, cuts off the patient's misguided efforts at magical repair, and directs the patient to realistic solutions and a healthy adaptation. This is the therapeutic task, and it can be successfully accomplished only if the therapist has the adaptational psychodynamics of the patient's disordered behavior readily at hand. This chapter provides these dynamics for the female patient with masculine aspirations.

CHAPTER 5

Psychotherapy of
Male Homosexuality:

Psychodynamic Formulation, Prognosis,
Selection of Patients, Technique

Introduction

THE purpose of this chapter is to describe a theoretical
approach to the treatment of male homosexuality. We
will focus on the narrow but definitive therapeutic goal
of establishing and maintaining pleasurable heterosexual
behavior in a homosexual patient. We will first formulate
a compact psychodynamic framework within which any
homosexual deemed suitable for psychotherapy can be
fitted, understood, and treated. We will then take up
prognosis, selection of patients, and special problems in
therapeutic technique. Our psychodynamic formulation

will be made in adaptational terms without recourse to Freudian concepts of instinct and energy. The reasons for dropping these concepts have been described in detail in a series of papers delineating the differences between an adaptational frame of reference and the Freudian instinctual frame of reference.[1]

We will also in this chapter bypass the issue of a genetically determined imbalance in maturation potentials that may underly the tendency to homosexuality. We do not know what role, if any, genetic factors play in the ultimate choice of sexual object. We do know, however, that arousal patterns can be readily influenced by cultural directives and individual experience. In clinical practice, all the homosexuals we have ever studied have had characteristic adaptive responses, unconsciously motivated, which were associated with the homosexuality. Our theoretical approach to treatment is based on the motivational breakdown of these adaptive responses.

Motivational Basis of Homosexual and Pseudohomosexual Behavior

Motivationally, the homosexual male seeks genital contact with other males not only for sexual reasons, but for nonsexual reasons as well. Three motivations are involved: homosexuality, dependency, and power. The homosexual motivation is the only one of these three that seeks sexual gratification as an end goal. The dependency and power motivations, however, as denoted by their names, seek completely different nonsexual goals, although they make use of the genital organs to achieve them. In consequence, their goals are often misconstrued as sexual, but in reality are not. For this reason, to facilitate psychodynamic reconstruction, these two motivations, dependency and power, have been designated the *pseudohomosexual* motivations.[2] Let us review briefly the developmental history of each of the three motivations that we have cited.

1. THE HOMOSEXUAL MOTIVATION.—Adaptationally, homosexuality is seen as a deviant form of sexual behavior into which a person is driven by the intrusion of fear into the normal heterosexual function. This concept was first proposed by Rado.[3] The fear takes its origin from excessive parental discipline in the developmental years of childhood. It appears especially to be fostered within the family constellation described by Bieber and his associates[4] where a son is caught between a controlling, dominating, overly intimate mother, on the one hand, and a detached, hostile, rejecting father, on the other. The fear may arise directly from actual intimidation of sexual behavior with its accompanying disciplinary threats implicit or explicit, or it may arise indirectly from nonsexual intimidation which inhibits assertion and undermines the growing boy's capacity to assume the masculine role. In either case, the child views heterosexuality as a dangerous transgression for which the fantasied punishments are castration and death. He perceives these punishments as coming either from the father or from the mother, usually from both. It makes little difference whether the initial focus of inhibition is sexual or nonsexual; ultimately, function in both areas will be impaired. This happens because inhibitions do not stay confined to the behavior area in which they were originally laid down, but the coincident loss of self-confidence tends to spread to other activities, and new inhibitions appear.

The child may respond to parental intimidation with a fear so great as to force a partial or complete withdrawal from sexual activity. Later, as the child grows, any heterosexual desires will revive the earlier fear, and an inhibition of normal sexual behavior is established. Such an inhibition may result in a homosexual choice of object. The person reacts with such intense fear in relation to a heterosexual object that he either fails in performance, or he succeeds mechanically, but experiences very little pleasure. His sexual need, however, continues unabated and is diverted to a "safer" object. This object is a homosexual one and derives its added safety from the reassuring presence of the penis, which allays the homosexual's castration anxiety.

Homosexuality, in this light, is a symptom of a neurosis, a defense against castration anxiety by the phobic avoidance of the female genital. The homosexual solution is only one of several solutions available to patients who suffer from this phobia. Other patients may retain their heterosexuality but make use of such protective devices as impotence, fetishism, exhibitionism, and so on. We cannot with certainty account for the specific choice of symptom, and it is not in the scope of this chapter to explore the problem.

2. THE DEPENDENCY MOTIVATION.—The unconscious wish for infantile dependency in adulthood is a confession of adaptive failure. The person who resorts to this wish is convinced that he lacks the adaptive equipment to satisfy his needs and to insure his survival. The developmental prototype for the dependency relationship is the relationship between the child and the mother. It is this relationship that the dependent adult seeks to reestablish. To this end he solicits help, support, protection. In extreme instances he wants another person to take over all responsibility for his welfare just as his mother did when he was a child. There are many traumatic situations in

childhood which perpetuate dependency attitudes in the adult and give rise to fantasies of magical repair. These have been reviewed recently[5] and need not be recapitulated in any detail here. It suffices for our purposes to note that dependency fantasies are a common feature in homosexual patients. They reflect the inhibitions of assertion which stem from parental intimidation in various behavior areas. Failures of assertion in dependent males are generally misinterpreted as failures in the masculine role, hence as femininity, and in the end as castration. The magical repair of these failures is most directly accomplished through the fantasied incorporation of the maternal breast. There is an alternative pseudohomosexual route, however, based on the equation, *penis = breast*. Here, the developmental prototype is the relationship between the child and the father. There are two ways in which this equation can be used, and both are acted out by the overt homosexual in the relationship with his partner. The first conceives of the father's penis as a feeding organ similar to the mother's breast. The reparative fantasy is then of sucking the penis in which the semen is equated with milk. The second involves incorporation of the father's penis, usually by mouth or per anum. In this way the dependent male undoes his castration, and the donor's "masculine" strength becomes available to him.

3. THE POWER MOTIVATION.—The nonassertive male may attempt to deny his weakness by acting out its opposite, a compensatory striving for power. Dependency strivings and power strivings can thus be considered opposite sides of the same coin. The power-driven dependent male structures relationships with other men in terms of dominance-submission. These relationships are then sym-

bolically placed in a male-female context in which the weaker male is forced to submit as a woman to the stronger male.* This unconscious conception of power struggles between men derives primarily from Oedipal rivalry with the father, to a lesser extent from sibling rivalry with brothers. In the course of development it is molded by cultural stereotypes, which represent masculinity as strong, adequate, and superior; femininity as weak, inadequate, and inferior. As we shall see, these fantasies about the achievement of power through domination of another man may play an important motivational role in the homosexual act.

All three motivational components that we have described exist in varying strengths in different homosexuals. The component in ascendency at any given time can be inferred during psychotherapy from the motivational context in which the patient's behavior becomes manifest. Variable combinations of these three ingredients provide an adaptational formula by means of which the behavior of any particular patient suffering from homosexuality, either overt or latent, can be understood. It should be emphasized that even in the overt homosexual, where the ultimate goal is orgastic pleasure, the sexual component does not operate in isolation, but always in association with the dependency and power components. The latter two not only enhance the motive force of the homosexual component, but also their relative strengths determine the psychosocial structure of the homosexual relationship as well as the physical mechan-

* The unconscious conception of dominance-subordination relationships in man, as inferred from dreams and fantasies of patients in psychotherapy, parallels dominance-subordination behavior in infrahuman primates. Maslow and his co-workers have done exhaustive studies of this parallel.[6]

ics of the homosexual act. Some of the most characteristic interactional patterns are demonstrated in the case
examples in chapter six.

Theory of Therapy

A theoretical approach to the treatment of male homosexuality derives logically from our understanding of the
motivational basis for the homosexual patient's behavior.
It is a clinically observable fact that the three motivations involved interact one with the other and are mutu-
ally reinforcing. Thus, any contact, either actual or
fantasied, by a homosexual with another man's body, particularly his genital, for purposes of dependency or power,
unfailingly acts as a sexual stimulant and cannot help
but intensify the wish for homosexual gratification. In
the opposite direction, homosexuality weakens the patient's masculine identification, inhibits his assertive capacities, and hence accentuates either passive strivings
for dependency or compensatory strivings for power, or
some combination of both. The end result in every homosexual is a vicious circle in which each motivation leads
to the other, irrespective of the motivational impetus with
which the circle may start.

The therapeutic task is to break up this circle, reverse
the homosexual pattern, and establish pleasurable heterosexual relations. This can be done by decreasing the intensity of the three motivations which propel the patient
toward genital contact with male objects, while simultaneously enhancing his sexual interest in women. The
primary focus of the therapy in terms of the ultimate
therapeutic goal must, of necessity, be on the homosexual
motivation and the phobic avoidance of the female genital. There is only one way that the homosexual can

overcome this phobia and learn to have heterosexual intercourse, and that way is in bed with a woman. In this
respect psychotherapy of homosexuality is essentially that
of any phobia. Sooner or later, the homosexual patient
must make the necessary attempts to have intercourse,
and he must make them again and again, until he is
capable of a sustained erection, penetration, and pleasurable intravaginal orgasm. The achievement of these end
goals can be facilitated by helping the patient to gain
insight into the unconscious fantasies which convert the
vagina into a source of danger. We must emphasize, however, that such insights are the means to an end; they
are not the end itself.

The secondary focus of the therapy falls on the pseudohomosexual motivations of dependency and power. To
decrease the intensity of these motivations the patient
must become more "masculine" by learning appropriate
patterns of assertion and increasing his self-sufficiency.
Here, again, the process can be aided by insight into
unconscious ideation. In some cases, merely an increase
in nonsexual assertion may prove sufficient to initiate and
maintain heterosexual behavior. This may occur even in
a brief therapeutic contact where major reliance is placed
on support, advice, and guidance, with little attempt
either by the patient or the therapist to explore the unconscious basis of the homosexuality. In our clinical experience, however, the great majority of homosexuals do
not respond to such a superficial approach nor do they
overcome their difficulties very quickly.

Prognosis

The prognostic indicators in the psychotherapy of male
homosexuals fall into two groups, some common for

symptom disorders in general, others specifically related to the symptom of homosexuality, itself. There is considerable overlapping between the two groups, and any assessment of treatability must take both into account. The most significant factors are discussed below. Our observations are based on clinical impression and hence are subject to revision through statistical analysis. We believe, however, in essence, they would prove to be accurate.

1. MOTIVATION.—A patient's motivation for seeking treatment is one of the most important indicators of prognosis because a genuine desire to get well can often surmount many negative features. We are not prepared to say why one patient has the will and another has not; we can only observe empirically that some have it and get well, while others lack it and stay ill. It is not difficult with most psychiatric patients, even in the first interview, to establish the sincerity or insincerity of their desire for change. Far more often than not, the accuracy of the evaluation is subsequently validated in therapy. Unfortunately, this is not the case with many homosexual patients. Assessment of motivation in a homosexual on first meeting is a tricky business.

There are, of course, some who, from the outset, forthrightly insist they do not want to give up their homosexuality, but seek help for other—often related—problems. These patients may perhaps be helped therapeutically, but they will usually remain homosexuals. Others, who come not voluntarily, but through family pressure or after a brush with the law, are momentarily bowing to higher authority. To the therapist, they present a managerial problem; only rarely can their homosexuality be treated. Cases such as these, where the motivation is negative, are clear cut, but they are in the minority.

Most homosexuals who come to the psychiatrist take the opposite tack. They state unequivocably that they wish to become heterosexual. Obviously, this is the group with the best prognosis, but their declaration cannot always be taken at face value. What the homosexual patient consciously claims he wants is not infrequently contradicted by his hidden unconscious desires, which become apparent only after he has gone into treatment.

It is well to remember that homosexuals are prone to periodic bouts of depression over their plight. Love relationships tend to be impermanent, and with the years, as youth passes, many a homosexual by the time he reaches thirty envisions a lonely future as an "old auntie." In despair, during such a low point, especially after a broken love affair, he may impulsively apply for treatment, but without serious intent. What he really wants is not heterosexuality, but a lasting homosexual relationship. A seemingly positive attitude in a homosexual at the start of a therapy, therefore, may be deceptive, and it may not be possible to evaluate the motivational factor until the patient's professed desire to change has been put to a therapeutic test. For this reason, the assessment of motivation as a prognostic indicator in many homosexuals, particularly those of long standing, should be made with considerable caution. This is especially true where many other indicators are doubtful.

2. EGO STRENGTH.—This term reflects the patient's response to environmental stress, past and present. From this standpoint, ego strength can be defined as the capacity for successful psychologic adaptation. Its evaluation is an essential factor in the prognosis of all psychiatric patients, not only homosexuals. A strong ego favors success in therapy, a weak ego does not. In spite of its importance, however, few psychiatrists evaluate ego

strength in any systematic way; instead, most rely on intuitive judgments that are often vague and ambiguous. We would recommend the method for evaluating ego strength recently devised by Karush and his co-workers.[7] They have drawn up a profile (Adaptive Balance Curve) of the ego's adaptive operations in various behavior areas. The profile not only permits assessment of ego strength or weakness in an individual patient, but also facilitates objective comparisons between different patients. Specific criteria are provided for rating adaptation in each of nine key integrative categories: dependency, general pleasure, genital pleasure, affectivity, mechanisms of defense, emergency emotions, guilt, psychopathology, and social interaction. A great merit of their method is that it can be applied clinically by all psychiatrists, irrespective of differences in theoretical persuasion.

3. SEXUAL IDENTIFICATION.—The sexual identification of homosexuals varies along a masculine-feminine axis. At one extreme is the homosexual, who assumes a feminine identification and gives up all pretense of meeting the requirements of the masculine role. He sees himself as weak and tends toward passivity. He dramatizes his wish to be a woman by cultivating quasi-feminine traits in voice, gesture, walk, and dress. The predominant pseudohomosexual component in his behavior is the dependency motivation. For him, the major adventitious purpose of the homosexual act is dependency-gratification, and, therefore, physically, he prefers to perform fellatio on his partner or be anally mounted by him. He accepts himself wholeheartedly as a homosexual and has no interest in change. We can say that the symptom of homosexuality within the framework of his personality is ego-syntonic.

At the other extreme of the axis is the homosexual

who assumes a masculine identification. He is driven to gratify his sexual need in a homosexual fashion because he is too frightened of women to perform heterosexually, but, notwithstanding, he rejects violently any representation of himself as feminine. His underlying unconscious wish is to be dependent, but he is terrified of passivity and its feminine connotation. He "proves" his masculinity by a masculine protest; that is, by exaggerating so-called masculine traits. He takes care to look manly, tends to be overaggressive, and is hypersensitive to any slight, real or imagined, that connotes femininity. In his overt behavior, therefore, the predominant pseudohomosexual component is the power motivation. As a result, he attempts to redeem his masculine failure through a compensatory domination of a weaker partner. He seeks to have men submit to his penis orally and anally, but generally refuses to accept the reverse role. He denies his own dependency at the expense of the weaker man. In this way, he not only satisfies himself sexually, but also enhances his deflated masculinity by making a woman out of his partner. The homosexual act, itself, is a confession of masculine failure, yet in this instance, the patient paradoxically uses it to affirm his masculinity. The term "paradoxical homosexuality" applies to cases of this kind. In such a homosexual, the symptom of homosexuality is ego-alien.

The great bulk of homosexuals fall between the two extremes. They have mixed—masculine and feminine—identifications. In some cases, the feminine identification is more prominent; in other cases, the masculine identification is more prominent. The poorer prognosis is associated with the higher degrees of feminine identification; or conversely, the better prognosis is associated with the higher degrees of masculine identification. In general, the mounters do better than the mounted. Thus, in our experience, as far as sexual identification is concerned, the best prognosis is found in the paradoxical homosexual.

4. SOCIAL IDENTIFICATION.—This factor is very closely related to sexual identification. The homosexual who has a feminine identification and accepts his homosexuality usually identifies himself socially as a homosexual. He openly enters into "gay life," socializes mostly with other homosexuals, and often lives with a homosexual partner. It is doubly difficult for homosexuals of this kind, who are intimately involved in homosexual society, to give up their homosexuality. Not only must they learn to relate to women sexually, but also they must sever established social ties and start anew in heterosexual circles. Most are ill suited for this task and have no desire to undertake it. They are confirmed homosexuals and remain so. Only a few in this group apply for therapy. Their prognosis is uniformly poor, and their motivation for treatment should always be held suspect. The outlook is much better for the homosexual who keeps his homosexuality hidden, practices it surreptitiously, and identifies himself socially as a heterosexual. This, of course, occurs only in homosexuals whose masculine identification is so strong that they struggle against their homosexual inclinations.

5. HOMOSEXUAL CONSOLIDATION.—Under this heading, we have included several factors that measure the degree to which the homosexuality is fixed as a symptom.

a. Age of Onset. First awareness of homosexuality usually occurs in pubescence, less often in adolescence. Prognostically, the later it occurs, the better. The worst outlook is found in those who claim they have been homosexual as far back as they can remember, never once having experienced a heterosexual impulse. In this connection, there are some homosexuals who give a specific history of homosexual arousal very early in childhood. For example, one patient remembered that he became sexually excited and experienced an erection when he was jiggled on his uncle's knee at the age of five. From then on, according to him, he was always interested in male bodies and never had a flicker of interest in women. Another patient with a homosexual boot fetish recollected a specific incident, again at the age of five, when he spent a few minutes with a gardener, became fascinated with his boots, and responded with an erection. We do not know whether such incidents actually happened when reported, or whether they are retrograde reconstructions of events occurring much later, but attributed to the earlier age. Clinically, in either case, such an early onset, whether actual or alleged, is a poor prognostic sign.

b. Duration of Symptom. In general, as with any symptom, the longer homosexuality has existed, the more difficult it is to alter. Younger patients, therefore, usually do better than older ones, but there are exceptions based on differences in motivation, all other factors being equal. The older patient who seeks treatment, has had his "kicks," as it were, and has grave doubts that he can find happiness through a homosexual way of life. He is tired of secrecy, the sense of difference from other men, and the loneliness. He longs for normalcy, for social acceptance, for a wife and children. His motivation for change has gradually hardened with the passage of time. The younger man, however, is still having his fling, and may not yet have reached sufficient maturity to look into the future and foretell what lies ahead of him. He still hopes he can make it as a homosexual. He may intellectually see the need for change, but emotionally his motivation may be luke-warm and remain so until a few more years have passed and hope has begun to dim.

c. *Exclusiveness*. The prognosis is usually poorer in the exclusive homosexual whose sexual experience has been with men only. It is better in those who made attempts to have intercourse with women before they gave up and settled exclusively for men, even if they failed. If the attempts were successful, the prognosis is further enhanced.

d. *Compulsiveness*. In a number of cases, we have seen a compulsive element where the patient is compulsively driven to commit the homosexual act to relieve emotional tension. There is a similarity here with the compulsive need to act out in sociopaths, alcoholics, drug addicts, and obsessive-compulsive neurotics suffering from compulsive rituals. In our experience, such compulsiveness is an unfavorable sign.

6. HETEROSEXUAL INTEGRITY.—Under this heading, we have included several factors that measure the homosexual patient's residual capacity for heterosexual behavior. Conversely, they tell us how crippled is the heterosexual drive.

a. *Capacity for Pleasurable Arousal*. Any degree of heterosexual interest, no matter how slight, is better than none. It is a good sign if a homosexual experiences pleasurable arousal with a woman and musters an erection, particularly if it leads to consummation through pleasurable orgasm. There are some homosexuals, however, who manage an erection, engage in intercourse, and achieve orgasms, but with little or no pleasure, even to the point of penile anesthesia. The loss of pleasurable sensation in such patients is a conversion reaction and indicates massive interference from heterosexual anxiety. Still, the prognosis is far better in these cases, where the patient at least performs mechanically even if he has no pleasure, than in those who cannot get aroused to begin with and hence do not perform at all.

b. Attitude toward Female Genital. One of the most accurate measurements of heterosexual integrity is the homosexual patient's attitude toward the female genital. The homosexual, who, in spite of his fears, is pleasurably aroused by it, wants to see it, feel it, and establish oral or genital contact with it will do well in therapy. His heterosexual drive has suffered minimal damage and is essentially intact. On the other hand, the homosexual, who experiences neither pleasure nor desire, and in addition is revolted by the female genital, not only emotionally, but often physically as well, will find it most difficult to alter his response. His heterosexual drive has been markedly damaged. In such patients, the negative attitude toward the female genital may be so ingrained that no amount of reconditioning will reverse it.

c. Nonexclusiveness of Homosexuality. There are some men, popularly known as "bisexuals," who are capable of pleasurable sexual relations with both men and women. The pseudohomosexual motivations are very prominent in their behavior and phobic anxiety about the female genital is held to a minimum. They are on the fence and have not yet decided on which side to cast their lot. Once committed to therapy, however, they usually do well. Foremost in this group prognostically are those patients whose sexual outlet is predominantly heterosexual and who only occasionally lapse into homosexuality. The outlook is especially good if they can limit their homosexual impulses to fantasy and thus keep them latent altogether.

d. Potency. As one would expect, potency disorders are

a common complication in homosexuals who attempt sexual relations with women. It is obviously more favorable to the prognosis if the patient is fully potent, but neither is it necessarily fatal if he is not. Much more serious than impotence in itself is an association with the two negative indicators: lack of pleasurable arousal with women and an attitude of revulsion toward the female genital. In the absence of these indicators, with effort, time, and patience, the impotence may eventually be overcome. In the presence of these indicators, however, the prospect is very bleak.

e. Nonsexual Relations with Women. In some homosexuals, the universal fear of the female genital is extended to include nonsexual relations with women. These homosexuals see women as hostile, all-engulfing, devouring monsters. They avoid them socially as much as possible and relate to them only with antagonism. The prognosis is worse in such homosexuals than in those who limit their perception of danger mainly to the genital and thus are better able to enjoy purely social relations with women.

f. Sexual Fantasies. A patient with a predominantly heterosexual fantasy life has a better prognosis than one with a predominantly homosexual fantasy life.

The prognostic indicators that we have discussed are summarized below in two contrasting columns, each representing an extreme, the most favorable on one side, the least favorable on the other side:

Favorable Prognosis	*Unfavorable Prognosis*
1. Strong motivation	1. Weak motivation
2. Strong ego strength	2. Weak ego strength
3. Masculine sexual identification	3. Feminine sexual identification
4. Heterosexual social identification	4. Homosexual social identification

5. Low degree of homosexual consolidation
   a. Late onset
   b. Short duration
   c. Nonexclusive
   d. Noncompulsive
6. High degree of heterosexual integrity
   a. Attracted to women sexually
   b. Sexual contact with women pleasurable
   c. Attracted by female genital
   d. Nonexclusive homosexuality. Has had heterosexual experiences
   e. Potent with women
   f. Enjoys nonsexual relations with women
   g. Predominant heterosexual fantasy life

5. High degree of homosexual consolidation
   a. Early onset
   b. Long duration
   c. Exclusive
   d. Compulsive
6. Low degree of heterosexual integrity
   a. Not attracted to women sexually
   b. Sexual contact with women not pleasurable
   c. Revolted by female genital
   d. Exclusive homosexuality. No heterosexual experiences
   e. Impotent with women
   f. Rejects nonsexual relations with women
   g. Predominant homosexual fantasy life

Selection of Patients

In any particular patient, the various indicators in each column, favorable or unfavorable, tend to cluster together. It is unusual to find anything like an even division. More commonly, the indicators are either predominantly favorable or predominantly unfavorable. What varies is the degree of favorability or unfavorability. Most of the homosexuals who seek treatment fall in the favorable category —some more, some less. Those in the unfavorable group do not often appear in the psychiatrist's office, and when they do, their motivation will usually not stand up to challenge. The problem of selecting homosexuals as patients for treatment, therefore, is solved for the most part by the homosexuals themselves. What it gets down to is simply this: those who seek treatment are candidates for treatment; those who don't are not. The crucial indicators are motivation and ego strength, both difficult to assess. It is well to remember that prognostic indicators are, in fact, just indicators, and that is all they are. They only indicate; they do not assure. In clinical practice, the margin of error in predicting success or failure in psychotherapy is a sizable one. Treatment is full of surprises, and there isn't a psychiatrist who has not been surprised, and more than once. Dubious cases sometimes improve, and hopeful cases sometimes fail. For this reason, we urge that every homosexual seeking treatment, whose motivation bears up in the initial interview, be given the benefit of the doubt and permitted to undergo a therapeutic trial. As for the rest, the confirmed homosexuals who wish only to be left alone—at the present state of our knowledge we have nothing to offer them. There is no way that a homosexual who does not wish to become heterosexual can be forced to change. We do not know how to do it therapeutically, nor can it be done by parental edict or by court order.

Special Problems in Therapeutic Technique

In this section, we will concentrate on the special problems of technique peculiar to the psychotherapeutic management of the homosexual patient. We will not be concerned here with the many technical problems that the homosexual shares in common with all other patients. In that category, we include the management of dependency conflicts and inhibitions of self-assertion. Rather, we will deal primarily with the problem of initiating and maintaining heterosexual relations in the most intransigent of homosexual patients, namely the exclusive homosexual, who has had no sexual experiences with women, or in the nonexclusive homosexual, who nevertheless prefers homosexuality to heterosexuality. Our remarks, however, will be generally applicable to all homosexual patients, to some extent or another, whatever their ilk.

The therapist must from the outset establish for the patient three fundamental assumptions on which the therapy is based:

1. Homosexuality is pathologic. It is not a natural biologic phenomenon.
2. The homosexual act is an overdetermined symptom with specific unconscious meanings.
3. Homosexuality is a treatable illness. Through treatment, the normal heterosexual direction of the sexual drive can be reestablished.

These assumptions provide the therapeutic framework within which the therapy is conducted. They must be reiterated again and again throughout the therapy. They are transmitted to the patient not only by the technical maneuvers of the therapist, but also by his attitude. Hope is contagious and is a necessary ingredient in any therapy. Not all psychiatrists, therefore, should treat homosexuality. Those who lack conviction that homosexuality is a treatable illness, but believe instead that it is a natural constitutional variant, should not accept homosexuals as patients.

Eventually, after the basic assumptions about homosexuality have been established, the patient inevitably gets to his fear of women. At this point, a few embark spontaneously upon heterosexual relationships. Most homosexuals, however, do not move very readily toward women. More often, the patient protests that he is not ready for sex with a woman. He is, of course, right. The therapist should reassure him that for the present he is only asked to see women socially, to date them; nobody is asking that he jump into bed with them. Later, when he is comfortable with a date, he will begin first to neck, then to pet, and eventually go even further, but certainly not now. If the patient is at all serious about treatment, he will accept this compromise and gradually, with some pressure from the therapist, if necessary, begin to go out. As a matter of fact, he may very well be eager to date socially because it gets him off the hook sexually, as far as women are concerned, at least for the time being.

The sexual undertones of social encounters with women, however, generate a steady flow of heterosexual anxiety. From time to time, therefore, in order to alleviate his distress, the homosexual patient may sporadically flee from women and act out homosexually with men. Afterwards he is always guilty, but rarely will this restrain him, no matter how good his intentions. His resolve needs reenforcement by the therapist. How is this best accomplished? In our opinion, the therapist should neither forbid nor condone this behavior. We do not look with favor upon interdiction, with or without the threat of termination, because we feel it is technically unsound. The homosexual is no different from any other patient. He, too, must defensively hang on to his symptom until he can overcome his anxiety and integrate normal patterns of behavior. Interdiction, therefore, may place an unbearable burden on him which he may shake off either by lying to the therapist or by running away from treatment altogether. We do not say there is no place for an ultimatum in the therapy of homosexuality. There is a place, just as in the therapy of other phobias, where the patient may be threatened with termination if he unduly procrastinates about entering the phobic situation. In other words, the homosexual patient should be given an ultimatum for insufficient efforts to perform heterosexually, not for his protective homosexual diversions.

How then should these homosexual episodes be managed? Our technique for discouraging homosexuality is to interpret it objectively as a symptom whenever it occurs. The therapist must show the patient how a flight into homosexuality is a defense that counteracts his fear of women. It is a regression, a manifestation of his resistance, and hence not to his advantage in the therapy. He will achieve his goals faster if he sticks to heterosexuality. Thus, again, our emphasis is to encourage heterosexuality, rather than to discourage homosexuality. In the course of therapy, the patient learns to interpret each homosexual act just as he learns how to interpret dreams. He pinpoints what precipitated the act and then he breaks it down into its motivational components. We hold him to such an exercise without fail every time he acts out, because silence, when a patient confesses a homosexual act, may be taken as tacit approval. He may then simply use the treatment as a catharsis, relieve his guilt, and blithely continue to act out.

The patient should not be encouraged in hasty attempts at intercourse. They increase his chances of failure, and in the long run make his task more difficult. Naturally, should he make an attempt, even though ill advised and irrespective of success or failure, he should be praised. However, it is preferable for him to wait until he is emotionally involved in a supportive relationship with a sexually healthy woman. Once he achieves this, the issue of sexual intercourse cannot long be avoided. If the patient, himself, does not raise the question, then the woman does; and if she does not, then, in the last resort, the therapist should raise it. At this point in the treatment, inevitably, there is a sharp upsurge of anxiety and a prolonged period of resistance may well ensue. The patient confronts the therapist with two big rationalizations: (1) he has sexual desire only for men, not for women; and (2) he is afraid he will not get an erection.

These are handled in accordance with the basic assumptions of the treatment. Thus, once more, we interpret any homosexual desire symptomatically as a displaced heterosexual drive. The therapist must insist that this drive is not missing, only impounded by fear, even though, for the moment, the patient feels little or nothing. Once the fear is removed, desire for women, and with it an erection, will appear. The patient's response to this interpretation is often a wishful one. He would be very happy to attempt intercourse, but the therapist must first relieve his anxiety and thus guarantee both arousal and performance. The answer to his demand is obvious. The anxiety will not disappear, nor will he learn to be potent in advance of going to bed with a woman, but only in the process of making the attempt. The sooner he tries, the faster he will learn there is nothing to fear.

The therapist has little choice during this period, but to wait out the patient's resistance, however long it may take. He reiterates the basic assumptions, exposes the patient's rationalizations, analyzes his unconscious fantasies of danger, and cuts off attempts at magic repair. Other than this, there is nothing more he can do, except threaten the patient with termination, a last ditch device, if he does not take action. How long the therapist should wait before resorting to such a drastic step is a matter of

clinical judgment. As a general rule, in cases of homosexuality, the resistance should be measured in years—
perhaps two or three, sometimes more—rather than in
months.

Once the stalemate is broken, the outlook is more favorable, but the difficulties are hardly ended. A few homosexual patients have surprisingly little trouble in their
initial attempts at intercourse or thereafter, and may even
be fully potent from the beginning. The majority, however
are not so successful, but are plagued by impotence in
its various forms. Many, at first, cannot achieve an erection, just as they feared, or if they achieve it, they cannot
maintain it. Others are more successful and manage penetration, but then suffer from premature ejaculation. A
universal complaint is diminution or absence of pleasurable sensation. The therapist must support the patient
through these failures and encourage him to try again,
since only by repetition will he ever become successful.
This is no easy task. We do it by converting the failure as
much as possible into a triumph. We emphasize the attempt, rather than the failure. We tell the patient right
now the important thing is that he tried, not that he fell
short of completion. We reassure him that failure at the
beginning was only to be expected; if he does not retreat,
but continues to try, eventually he will be successful.
With shaky patients, who are ready to give up, the therapist should commit the magic omnipotence with which
he is unconsciously endowed in the transference, and guarantee ultimate success, contingent, of course, on further
efforts by the patient.

Full potency in itself is not a final solution to a homosexual patient's problems. It is too narrow a therapeutic
goal. It is doubtful that heterosexuality, once established,
can be sustained without the framework of a total relation-

ship with a woman. Theoretically, it may be possible, but practically, the temptations are too great. A successful marriage, therefore, is the ultimate therapeutic goal. It is the patient's best insurance against residual homosexuality, since it drains off his sexual need through heterosexual activity. Furthermore, it provides him with emotional support, as well as social companionship, and it gives him a sense of personal fulfillment as a man that is rooted in the satisfactions of being a husband and a father.

CHAPTER 6

Case Studies of
Male Homosexuality

Introduction

THIS chapter demonstrates the clinical utilization of the
psychodynamics and the theory of therapy formulated in
the previous chapter. We will describe three successfully
treated male homosexuals with follow-ups of five or more
years. We have organized the clinical data in order to
demonstrate best the psychodynamics as they emerge in
the course of phychotherapy. In keeping with the purpose
of the previous chapter, our emphasis will fall on the
meaning of the patient's behavior as a basis for therapeutic technique, rather than on the technique itself. We will
try, however, to indicate at least some of the more important technical maneuvers, how they relate to the psychodynamics, and why they are undertaken.

Case 1.

A 30-year-old, <u>unmarried Jewish man</u>, employed as a junior executive in an advertising agency, came to treatment because of mounting anxiety in his work. His difficulties arose from extreme competitiveness with his colleagues, particularly male authorities, which created so much overt hostility that his job was in jeopardy. In the course of the history the patient casually revealed that he was an active homosexual. It was clear that he did not in any way associate his homosexuality with the problems at his job, nor was it a factor in his decision to seek treatment.

The patient was short and slightly built, but somewhat big of hip. He was dapper, good-looking, and meticulously dressed. His speech, manner, and dress were all studied in the prep school tradition, which, however, was not part of his background. As a junior executive in an advertising agency, he met all the generalizations attributed to Madison Avenue. He was the youngest of three boys from a middle-class family. The father was a moderately successful professional man, but weak, inadequate, and totally intimidated by the mother, who was the dominant member of the household. She was sharp-tongued, aggressive, self-willed, and obviously brighter than the father. Despite this severe picture, the patient was much fonder of her than of the father, the implication being that strength at least could be respected. The weakness of the father left nothing but contempt.

Throughout his childhood the patient had a constant feeling that he was not "manly" like other boys. First of all, he was small and at a competitive disadvantage physically, and, second, his mother resented never having a daughter and attempted to feminize her sons, particularly the patient, since he was the youngest. She kept him in girl's clothes until three, insisted he wear his hair long for several years more, and taught him to do feminine chores, such as sewing, cleaning, and cooking. He dated girls all through high school, but, at the same time, as an adolescent, began to be plagued by homosexual thoughts and feelings which he tried to push out of his mind. At 19 he was drafted. The Army was in every way a traumatic experience for him. He was frightened, bewildered, and felt "different" from the other men, most of whom were larger and more aggressive. Some of them taunted him about his hips and said that he was built like a woman. It was during this period in the Army, when he felt particularly unmanly, that he had his first homosexual relationship. It followed a specific pattern which has been a prototype for all subsequent activity. He insists first on satisfying his partner by manual masturbation. He then mounts the partner per anum and performs anal intercourse on him, but he will not permit himself to be anally penetrated. He thus plays the dominant masculine role in the relationship. In this way, he not only satisfies himself sexually, but also enhances his deflated masculinity by making a woman out of his partner. His homosexual relationships have been mostly transient, though in a few instances they have lasted for several months.

The patient's heterosexual experience was limited to two occasions. In high school he petted with a girl and got pleasure from it, but there was no attempt at intercourse and he never had an orgasm. His only experience with intercourse occurred at 23, when an older woman tried to seduce him. He was frightened and refused. At this point in his life he was already an active and confirmed homosexual. She persisted until he reluctantly went to bed with her. They had intercourse one time and he performed successfully, though mechanically and without pleasure. He had no further sexual contacts with women until he entered therapy.

The patient was treated on the couch three times a week for three years for a total of 347 hours. The first major therapeutic maneuver occurred within the first few interviews and arose implicitly from the adaptational concept of homosexuality. As the patient was giving his history and registering his complaints, the therapist asked him why he did not list homosexuality as one of the symptoms he wished to have corrected. The patient seemed bewildered. It had never occurred to him that homosexuality was a neurotic symptom, nor that one went to a psychiatrist to have it cured. His brother, a homosexual like himself, was also in psychoanalysis, and his analyst felt homosexuality was an inherited way of life that could not be altered and hence was of no particular therapeutic interest. The therapist stated unequivocally that he could not agree with this position, since he considered homosexuality a psychiatric illness which could be treated by psychotherapeutic means. The patient seemed genuinely confused, anxious, and yet delighted as was evidenced by a dream he reported the following day:

He returned to the lobby of the building in which he lived only to find it completely rebuilt overnight. Everything looked elegant, shiny, strong, and new. He was amazed at the transformation.

He felt the dream expressed his expectation that he might undergo a similar miraculous transformation, shed his homosexuality, and emerge from therapy a full-fledged heterosexual. The rather marked suggestibility of the patient was characteristic throughout treatment. It caused great difficulty in the later stages when he had to come to grips with his magical expectations, but at the beginning it served to mobilize intense activity toward a heterosexual existence. The assumption by a therapist that homosexuality is a developmental phenomenon and a treatable disease is basic to an adaptational therapy. Such an assumption, when communicated to a patient, can be a powerful therapeutic tool because it inevitably arouses hope that the deviant pattern can be altered.

In the second month of therapy the patient spontaneously began to date girls, although he made no attempt to get sexually involved with them. The dating was accompanied by constant anxiety which in the sessions was invariably associated with his father's weakness in the face of his mother's strength. He then became aware that there was an earlier time in his childhood when he had viewed the father as a superman, and his disillusionment had produced great resentment. The therapist wondered what validity this weakness of his father had in his present life as an adult. Why did it still invoke the rage and frustration of his childhood? What possible effect could his father's strength or weakness have on his difficulties with women? Ultimately, such confrontations led the patient to recognize his own fears of standing up to the mother. He needed to enlarge the father, who then would protect him from the mother, and by extension from all women. His present fear of women, therefore, not only recapitulated the original fear of his mother, but also revived his anger with the father for failing to protect him. This insight led to increased anxiety, a feeling of depression, and a sense that he "had nobody."

He attempted to overcome his fear of women by forcing

himself to engage in sex play with his dates. He was chagrined to find that fear so inhibited his aggressiveness that he felt more unmanly than ever. Nevertheless, he persisted and soon began to see a young woman, N., regularly. One night, aware of his failure to carry through sexually with her, even though she obviously was willing, he had the folowing dream:

He was with N. They were embracing. She petted his forehead and said, "Why don't you pluck your eyebrows?"

This dream made clear to him for the first time how he equated a lack of "masculine" aggressiveness with femininity. He responded in his characteristic way by attempting to disprove this equation through intercourse with N. He could not sustain an erection, and the attempt proved a failure. Encouraged by the therapist, he continued to try, and finally, one month later, he successfully consummated the act. He exultantly described his success as a "real seduction" in which he took the "masculine, aggressive" role. His triumph ushered in a period of successful sexual relations with N. Except for occasional prematurity, he had no further potency problems, and he experienced increasing pleasure in his orgasms. At the same time, in therapy, he became more and more resistant. He tended to deny homosexual feelings and resisted discussions of those he could not deny. After six months of treatment, he felt he was cured: He was ready to marry the girl, his problem on the job had disappeared, and he was free of anxiety. He said, "I look back on my homosexual life as something of the past. I guess I was just sowing my wild oats and now I'm ready to settle down."

The patient's rapid improvement had all the earmarks of a transference "cure." In his opening dream he had already indicated his magical expectations from therapy.

Apparently, he had acted on them and, in the transference, had supplanted the original weak father with a stronger one represented by the therapist. Thus, magically armed with the latter's strength, he sufficiently overcame his fear of women to embark on his heterosexual adventures, but the fear was hardly resolved, nor were its unconscious origins understood. None of these dynamics was interpreted to the patient during this period. As long as the transference was useful in mobilizing heterosexual activity it was thought best to leave it alone. With sexual inhibitions of this kind, nothing succeeds like success, and after his successful involvement the transference would eventually have to be faced, as indeed it was.

In the period that followed, the patient began increasingly to complain about his girl friend, who began to emerge as a very aggressive type. Concomitantly, he expressed more and more hostility toward his mother, with whom unfortunately the girl had much in common. She also had a history of relationships with homosexual men and was aware of the patient's homosexual background. As time went on, the focus of the therapy became the aggressive woman, his involvement with his mother, and the increasing difficulties he was having with N. All of these came to a head with a nightmare:

He was driving his car and skidded on some dog feces. He swirled around and around. N. was seated next to him. She was having a good time and enjoying it. Then he hit a lamp post which broke into two. The top part fell away, but the bottom part shot up through the floorboard right under him and he was in danger of being impaled on it. He woke up in great anxiety.

The dream resulted from a bitter argument the patient had with his girl friend in which she disparaged his manliness and taunted him as a homosexual. That same day, while walking together, he had stepped into some dog feces on the sidewalk. This was a key dream in the patient's analysis because it revealed the unconscious fantasies responsible for his fear of women. He associated to the dream for weeks, producing peripheral, confirming dreams, until gradually he understood its meaning. The dream is couched in sexual terms and represents intercourse with a woman as a dirty, potentially dangerous act. It defines not only the penalties for sexual assertion with a woman, but, since it was prompted by a quarrel, for nonsexual aggression against her as well. In either case, the woman can castrate the man, appropriate the penis for herself, and then, as a phallic woman, force the man to submit in a feminine fashion to her domination by shafting him per anum with her penis.

The patient felt disenchanted with N. and began to detach himself from her. She protested vehemently and became more abusive than ever. Her behavior stimulated renewed memories of his father's weakness, but now he saw the weakness as a product of his mother's destructiveness. She had castrated the father and upsurped his role as a male. He feared if he continued his relations with women the same thing could happen to him. For this reason he felt ambivalent about becoming a man. Perhaps it was better to remain a homosexual after all. At least it was safer, since another man already had a penis and would not need his. In this period of disengagement from N. he explored his many fantasies of the woman as castrator and dominator. He dropped N., momentarily avoiding women altogether, and thought longingly of homosexuality, but restrained himself from acting on the thought.

Up to this point the patient had struggled mainly to

free himself from the crippling distortion that all male-female relationships were duplications of the phallic-mother-castrated-father and the phallic-mother-castrated-child prototypes. His competitive difficulties with men had been checked and held in abeyance by his initial rapid success with women, but now, as he began to date again, his pseudohomosexual problem emerged in full force. He dated a great variety of women, seduced them as quickly as he could, and then discarded them. He returned in his sessions to the competition at work, talked of rivalry with his brothers, and of competition with men in general. Gradually, an Oedipal trend emerged in which he saw himself in conflict over women not only with his father, but also in the transference with the therapist. He had repetitive dreams of rivalry with his father for his mother. The following castration dream was typical of this period in the therapy:

He saw a huge crocodile floating down a river. Suddenly it grabbed hold of a small snake. The next thing he knew he had his hand in a toilet and was pulling out the snake.

He identified the crocodile as the father (huge penis) and himself as the snake (small penis). The penalty for attempting access to his father's territory, the river (mother's vagina), is castration and death. He saves himself by pulling his penis out of the mother's vagina (the toilet or "dirty hole").

As he examined his Oedipal rivalry, the patient began to talk of his father with less hostility and then turned to him for love. At the same time he was surprised to find a rise in homosexual desire despite the fact that he was eminently successful in his heterosexual life. Here he produced the first of several dreams of dependency on the therapist:

He was talking to the therapist and told him of his increased homosexual feelings. As he related them, he broke down and wept. The therapist said, "You better come home and spend some time with me," and he became one of a group of children who lived at the therapist's house.

In his associations, the patient again expressed his old resentment toward the father, who had never satisfactorily taken care of him. He wished now that he could be dependent on the therapist, but paradoxically, the idea of being dependent on a man, even though he wanted it, was distasteful to him and made him angry. It served only to confirm his sense of inadequacy, made him feel less masculine, hence feminine, and, in the end, castrated. The validity of this symbolic sequence was bolstered for him by a number of dreams where, through fellatio, he sucked strength from a stronger man's penis and so, himself, became powerful. In another series of dreams, he was dissatisfied with his penis, saw it as deficient, and borrowed or stole a new penis from more favored men. It became clear to him that homosexuality was not just a means of sexual gratification, but also a magical way of borrowing another man's penis for his own use.

In the next few months, the patient came to grips with his ambivalence toward men—the competitiveness and the dependency. He explored their developmental origins, their dynamic interconnections—one with the other, and the relation of both to his homosexuality. He began to understand that his hyper-aggressiveness was a compensatory attempt not only to assert his manliness and ward off castration by the father, but also to deny his dependency upon him. In essence, he learned how the mechanisms we described earlier in Chapter 5 in the section on motivation applied specifically to him. He learned also that he need not look upon all men as his father, any more than he need look upon all women as his mother. Finally, he began to see that his ultimate answers lay neither in compensatory aggression with men, nor in passive dependence, nor in homosexuality, but in self-sufficiency, equality in relationships, and heterosexuality. Gradually, as he understood these many things, he became less competitive with his father, with the therapist, and with other men, and his homosexual urges subsided.

He seemed to understand clearly the direction in which he had to move, but he was not quite ready to give up his dependency. The therapist, through his interpretation, had frustrated his attempts to be dependent on him. The patient thereupon took a step backwards and resumed the relationship with N., the girl who was a prototype of his mother. He had not seen her for more than a year, but they quickly began to fight as though they had never been apart. He wondered why he had gotten reinvolved. Were there reasons beyond the unresolved dependency? He soon found his answer in a dream in which he saw his mother as a whore with red lights attached to her house. He felt this related to his mother's seductive behavior with him, which he always found disgusting. At the same time, he realized he must have been attracted by it, or he would never have persisted so long with N. This led into his Oedipal feelings toward his mother, which, in turn, revived the Oedipal rivalry with his father. He worked through both aspects of his Oedipus complex and again the relationship with N. was terminated, as therapy settled down to many of the themes that had been previously dealt with.

The following year saw great changes in the patient's behavior. He became much less competitive at work and also much more successful. He began to date less hysterically. It was no longer important to date and have intercourse with every attractive woman he met. A marked alleviation of his competitiveness occurred after the interpretation of a particularly revealing dream:

There was a man screaming in anger. He was outraged and frustrated, and upset. He was the owner of the Chrysler Building. It was in the midst of construction, and he had just received word that a start had been made on the Empire State Building, which would be bigger. Even before his building was completed it was going to be only second best.

The patient recognized that this dream represented his extreme competitiveness wherein he aspired always to be the number one man, the biggest and the best, in any competition. As always, he made use of the penis and its size as the ultimate symbol of masculinity.

Shortly after this, the patient met L. and began an affair with her which eventually led to his marriage. During the closing months of treatment, sexual relations with L. became extremely pleasurable, and his homosexual impulses abated almost completely. Therapy was terminated just before he married L., and the patient felt quite secure that homosexuality was a thing of the past for him. He was seen in a follow-up four years later during a business crisis in which he felt his job was threatened. He had had a mild outbreak of both homosexual and pseudohomosexual fantasies, but he felt he understood them, and he was certain they would be transitory, which in fact they were. He was happy in his marriage, more relaxed, much less aggressive in his manner, and enormously successful vocationally. A year later all was still going well, and, in addition, he and his wife had a child.

The patient just described was somewhat unusual in that he spontaneously embarked on sexual relationships with women. His anxiety was limited, hence not too difficult to surmount, and he required a minimum of support, encouragement, and direction by the therapist. In contrast, most homosexuals do not move so readily toward women, but resist, delay, and procrastinate, often to such an extent that resolution of the phobic avoidance becomes a major technical problem. In this respect, the next patient, who made a prolonged attempt to avoid sexual contact with women, is the more typical.

Case 2.

This patient sought help specifically because of his dissatisfaction with homosexuality. He had been discharged from the Army for homosexuality, which was humiliating enough, but even worse was his subsequent arrest while attempting a homosexual pickup. His object, unfortunately, proved to be a detective in disguise. A few days spent in jail gave him quite a scare. He was released and put on probation when he promised to seek treatment.

He was 23 years old, over six feet tall, good-looking, and completely masculine in his appearance. He took great pride in the fact that he was not recognized on sight as a homosexual. His dress varied from a pressed work-day suit to a turtleneck black sweater and sloppy pants. He had little interest in his job as a stock clerk in a garment firm, and even less idea of what he wanted to do with his future working life. He lived alone and his social existence was a chaotic one, characterized by impulsive midnight swims and hitchhiking. He considered this made him quite unique and he was very proud to be known as a bohemian.

He grew up in a big city, the younger of two brothers. His parents were not close, argued a great deal, and, according to the mother, had married only because neither could find any one better. The mother weighed 300 pounds and had many ailments associated with her extreme obesity. She ran the house like a dictator and at the same time played the role of a martyr, referring incessantly to her imminent death and the many sacrifices she had made for the children. She always demanded of the patient, as the youngest son, that he do feminine household chores like cooking and ironing. She regularly hit the patient for disobedience until he was 15, when he threatened to hit her back. She was better educated than the patient's father and scorned him as her inferior. The father, a hard-drinking truckdriver, spent most of his evenings away from home. The mother, in the father's absence, made the boy her confidant in her ceaseless complaints about her husband. The patient was never close to his brother, a heterosexual, who married young to get away from the family.

In his earlier years, though not happy, he had been an obedient child and a good student. His homosexual history went back to childhood fantasies of a Cinderella-like nature in which he was a girl. His first actual homosexual memory was an incident, when he was eight, of mutual masturbation with his brother in the shower. From 13 until he went into the Army at 18, he was involved in every possible homosexual practice. He would often pick up older men and be paid by them, and he had one sustained relationship with such an older man during his last year in high school. His feverish homosexual activity interfered seriously with his studies and his marks suffered, but he did manage to graduate. He had frequent fantasies of running away from home and did try it once at 16 only to be found and brought back a few hours later. Now, while he said he wished amicable relations with his family, he was concerned with impressing people that he was independent, and he had even gone so far as to let some of his friends think that both his parents were dead.

After his Army discharge, the patient entrenched himself in his homosexual way of life. His preferred partners were generally well-built young men of his own age, and the actual sexual contacts were one-night affairs in which the patient played both the active and passive roles, orally and anally. Most recently he took only the active role in these relationships and refused to reciprocate. This was a source of pride to him as he considered it more manly and less degrading. He expressed concern that he had never felt love either for a man or woman, but had been a lone wolf all of his life. He had always assumed a big brother role with the few girls he knew. His one attempt at heterosexual intercourse was initiated by a much older woman, a lesbian, but was unsuccessful because he could not get an erection.

This patient was treated twice a week, at first sitting up for 49 sessions, then on the couch for a total of 268 sessions over a 3½-year period. He was discharged, but for reasons to be noted later, subsequently reentered treatment for six months. The second time he was seen 47 times, again twice a week and on the couch. He began therapy initially with an account of his feelings, attitudes, and anxieties about women. Soon, spontaneously, he went out on a few dates, but his efforts were desultory, and he drew back from any sexual involvement with the most transparent rationalizations. Most evident was his desire to ingratiate himself with the therapist through success with women, but this motivation served the needs of the therapy and at the beginning was deliberately not analyzed. Instead, his rationalizations for avoiding involvements with women were repeatedly pointed out. When, early in therapy, he hopefully suggested that his homosexuality might be inherited and hence not amenable to treatment, he was told in a forthright manner that this was not so.

For several months he would move toward women, become frightened, and run to a homosexual encounter. He was desperately afraid that he would not be able to function sexually with a woman, and if he tried and failed, it would only confirm his fear that he was not a man. His first dream expressed this anxiety about his masculinity. He dreamed he was taking off and putting on a Scotch kilt and some girl was laughing at him. He spoke of his apprehension about a dance he planned to attend in order to meet some girls. He feared that he might not be able to muster an erection while dancing, and if this were noticed by the girl it would reflect badly on his masculinity.

Finally, after much procrastination, in an outburst of courage, he impulsively went to bed with a prostitute. At first he did not have an erection, but then she was able to arouse him and they had intercourse. That night, in spite of his success, he had a disturbing dream:

He was in the woods. He was a male fox among many others and one of the foxes inserted anally into him. Then all the foxes, including the patient, changed into men.

He was upset at having such a "homosexual" dream, especially in the wake of his first successful heterosexual experience. His associations led to a pseudohomosexual aspect of the dream. It had been no triumph to "buy" a woman. She had taken charge of everything and had made him feel like a little boy. It had intensified the feeling that he always had anyway that his penis was too small. The therapist asked what all this had to do with the anal mount that occurred in the dream. The patient answered that in his homosexual contacts he came across men with large penises and he felt that through anal insertion he got some of their masculinity from them. The therapist pointed out the magical quality of this maneuver and emphasized that his sense of adequacy as a man depended on the establishment of successful relations with women. Attempts at magical repair through homosexual contacts, therefore, were not in the service of the therapy.

By the end of the first year, the therapy was gaining momentum and he was dating several girls regularly. He had not yet made another attempt at intercourse, but his self-confidence was growing every day. The confidence spilled over into other behavior areas, and he gave up his midnight swims and his hitchhiking. He explained that he felt better able to think of himself as a man and had less need to be a "character" in order to acquire status. He enrolled in an evening college to make up credits so that he could take a degree in architecture. Meanwhile he got a better paying job during the day doing cabinet work. Many of the nonsexual motives of his homosexual activity had been defined, but the unconscious ideas behind his fear of women had yet to emerge. They did not remain hidden very long. The patient soon embarked on his second successful sexual relationship, but the affair lasted only a few days when he complained to the therapist of mounting anxiety and stopped seeing the girl. At this point, a nightmare revealed at least one source of his phobic anxiety.

He and his mother were lying together. He had only a towel wrapped around him. She began to play with his penis. He asked her to stop, which she did, but then he felt as though his penis had been cut. He looked down and was horrified to see that she had somehow folded his penis and made a vagina out of it.

He had spent the night of the dream with his parents and felt that he had behaved in an overly submissive way with his mother. Whenever this happened, it revived his old childhood feeling that she had crushed his masculinity. Thus, in the dream, she castrates him and makes him into a woman. He was shown how the fear of castration by his mother had been extended to women in general and was affecting his current behavior. In his associations to the dream, the patient made no mention of erotic interest in the mother. The therapist, therefore, did not deal with this aspect of the Oedipus complex.

He began an affair with another girl, but in a state of anxiety abruptly abandoned her, just as he had the first girl. Once more he began to avoid going out with women. He then had a series of dreams with homosexual content. In a typical dream he was fighting off a man at the door, who wanted him to perform fellatio. He said he had no particular difficulty recently in controlling his homosexual impulses, but he was troubled by his lack of desire for women. He felt under therapeutic pressure to find one. The man at his door, he felt, was really the therapist. It was decided not to deal with the projected homosexual wish in this dream, but to focus instead on his feeling of being forced by the therapist to relate to women or risk the therapist's displeasure if he did not. Up to this point, his need to please the therapist had been of great service in mobilizing his efforts. Now, however, he saw this need as a submission to the therapist, and it was interfering with his desires for women, rather than facilitating them. The therapist felt, therefore, that this was the time to interpret the patient's misconception that he was in therapy for anyone's sake but his own. The patient's first reaction to the interpretation was to be discouraged, a not uncommon reaction to an interpretation of this kind. He took it to mean that his sexual conquests of women were not genuine, but were due somehow to the therapist. He was reassured on this point, that it was really he who had succeeded, and after a few days of discouragement, he tried again, this time with J., an older woman, who lived in his apartment building. He liked her very much and soon made sexual advances to her to which she responded. He then became anxious, alternated between hesitation and desire, and, as before, wanted to run away.

After an evening of petting, he had the following dream:

He had somehow injured his pinky and was taken to a hospital. It turned out that his mother was in charge of the dispensary. She said she had orders for his execution. J., however, pleaded that he be spared.

He related the castration and the execution to a fear that his mother would disapprove of his relationship with J. He wondered also if the protection he would get from J. would compensate for giving up his mother. The therapist commented on his excessive concern for his mother's approval, and he pointed out that at his age he was entitled to make his own decisions. This was felt to be a better way of mobilizing him toward the relationship and preferable to stressing what was also true: His fear that J. would be a castrating woman like his mother.

Apparently, he felt challenged by the therapist, and the next time he saw J. they had sexual intercourse. This time he stayed in the relationship for several months, his first sustained sexual affair. He reviewed again and again through free associations and dreams his central anxiety that he would be castrated by the woman. He experienced greater pleasure in the sexual act, and he became increasingly confident about his sexual performance. The relationship eventually came to an end because J. met a man her own age and decided to marry him. By the time it was over, however, the patient had matured a great deal.

He then met R., whom he found very attractive and who seemed to like him. Within a few days he was head over heels in love and began to talk excitedly of marriage. The therapist attempted to slow him down and cautioned him against any hasty action. The patient nodded assent and in the next interview stated that he had restrained himself with R., but he felt when they parted that she had been disappointed with his lack of enthusiasm. He then reported a dream:

He was standing with a girl. An ambulance hit him from the rear and crushed him. His hand was severed and went flying.

He identified the girl as R. and the ambulance as the therapist. The dream was traceable to his suppressed anger against the therapist for suggesting that he take it easy with R. He had been disinclined to follow this advice, but feared that the therapist would be angry if he did not. The dream symbolizes his submission to the therapist, a more powerful male. As a result, he is anally raped, castrated, and loses the girl. The submissiveness was a cover-up for his rage which he had not dared to express openly. The dream led to a prolonged review of his dependent submissiveness to men and his underlying resentment toward them because of it.

Over the next few weeks his relationship with R. developed at a rapid rate. All his earlier sexual anxieties returned, and he became frantic about his performance with her. She had evidently not had sexual relations before, but was desirous of having them with him. At first he was completely incapable to get an erection. Then in a few weeks, he began to get erections, but would lose them before entry or immediately after. In his therapeutic sessions, he saw his relationship with R. as a defiance of his mother. He had repeated dreams in this vein. A typical one follows:

He was in bed with R. The phone rang and it was his mother. She wanted to know what he was doing. He was furious and yelled that it wasn't her business. He noticed in the bed that R. was covered and he was not. A maternal aunt was there and shook her head disapprovingly. He felt guilty and covered himself.

The night before this dream intercourse with R. had not worked out, but he had been closer to success than ever before. R. had been disappointed, but helpful, as always. He saw her sometimes as a maternal figure, who gave him the love and comfort that he had wanted from his mother, but had never gotten. He wondered if an incest taboo was still inhibiting him, and his associations turned again to the Oedipus complex and its many ramifications. The therapist interpreted his need to "cover up" as a means of warding off his mother's disapproval of his sexual behavior. Gradually, his self-confidence returned, his performance improved, and soon they were having intercourse without any difficulties whatsoever. He asked her to marry him and she accepted.

They planned a wedding in a few months and announced their engagement. His mother was dissatisfied with certain details of the wedding arrangements and made unreasonable threats not to come unless they were changed. His fury made it possible to work through more definitely his angry dependency toward her. He dreamed:

He was in a maternity ward. A baby was being born to his mother. She was near death. The umbilical cord was knotted and a doctor untied it.

The dream followed a weekend in which he had sexual relations with R. and she had bled a little. His mother always reminded him of how much she had gone through because of his cesarean birth. His anger with her and the guilt over hurting her hid his anxiety about separation from her. In the dream, he is afraid that if he severs the cord and leaves her it will kill her, but actually it is his own survival without her that concerns him.

He was chagrined to discover his hidden wish to remain dependent on the mother and took a step designed to prove his independence. He came in and announced that he and R. had secretly gotten married. He had told no one, not even the therapist. They intended to keep it a secret and go through with the scheduled wedding in a few weeks as planned. He was quite pleased with himself. This way he felt he could have his cake and eat it, too.

The patient remained in treatment for another six months. He entered a school of architecture on a full-time daily basis while his wife worked as a schoolteacher. The remainder of the therapy was concerned mostly with further resolution of his dependency problem as it emerged in his new role as a husband. There were minor problems between him and his wife, which were adjusted without much difficulty, and when treatment was terminated their relationship seemed to be a stable one. He was then seen once a year for the next seven years as a follow-up. At one point, after 2½ years, he reentered treatment for several months because of difficulties at school. He was not working well because he felt his teachers did not sufficiently appreciate his efforts. This remnant of his underlying dependency on parental figures was again analyzed with a resultant improvement in his school work. He went on to graduate and currently is employed as an architect. The marriage has fulfilled its earlier promise and continues to be stable. He states he has not been aware of any recurrence of homosexual desires, and he considers homosexuality completely a part of his past. He has had no potency problems, and he feels that his sexual life with R. has exceeded his fondest expectations. He has also begun a family and in his last follow-up reported that he had a son.

Case 3

This case presents an interesting example of the individual, who is neither an exclusive nor an overt homosexual, except for one brief episode, but rather struggles with latent, repressed, and suppressed homosexual feelings within the framework of an apparently heterosexual existence. The patient was a 24-year-old medical student, a tall, good-looking, fluent, intelligent young man with a marked boyish air which he cultivated and capitalized on. He entered treatment with two groups of complaints. The first was concerned with his "overdependence" on his family. The second was an "inability to form a lasting relationship with a woman."

The patient came from a moderately well-to-do family. His father was a successful lawyer, a very hard worker, scrupulous, conscientious, and exacting. He was not very demonstrative, and the patient always felt he was rather cold. He was a very big man, six feet four inches. The patient always wanted to be as tall as his father, but never quite made it, falling short by four inches. As a result, even though he was six feet tall, and hence well above average in height, he did not think of himself as tall. He and his father were congenial, but not close. He was much closer to his mother, but this was a very mixed blessing. She was warm, giving, and extremely devoted, but so overprotective that the patient felt she "smothered" him with her love. There was one sibling, a sister two years younger, with whom the patient never felt close.

It soon became apparent that the second group of complaints were much more specifically sexual than the patient had originally been willing to admit. It was true that he had been unable to form "lasting relationships" with women, but above and beyond that there were marked disturbances in his sexual behavior, revealed particularly in his masturbatory fantasies. The most frequent of these fantasies went back to his early childhood, as far back as he could remember. In them he identified himself as a woman and imagined that he possessed female genitalia and female secondary sexual characteristics. Occasionally, he actually dressed in woman's underclothes in order to enhance his sense of identification with the opposite sex. When he used this fantasy in masturbation he was never conscious of a sexual object, either homosexual or heterosexual; he simply concentrated on the image of himself as a woman. There were two other masturbatory fantasies, however, in which the sexual object was clearly discernible. One was heterosexual with a thinly veiled Oedipal constellation; that is, he saw himself as an intimidated, weakened slave of a strong queenly woman, who ordered him about and humiliated him, but in return offered protection, love, and sexual gratification. The second was homosexual and consisted usually of mutual masturbation, less often of oral and anal activity in which he generally assumed the passive role.

His overt sexual relations in reality were almost exclusively heterosexual. He dated many girls with whom he necked and petted. He inevitably got aroused, experienced an erection, and seemingly enjoyed these activities, but he always stopped short of permitting himself to ejaculate. He had intercourse only once with a girl who was exceptionally seductive and made it difficult for him to retreat. He managed to carry out the act, but he was very frightened and got only limited pleasure from it. In spite of his homosexual fantasies, he had had only a single transient homosexual contact. It occurred at 21 when he was picked up by an older man, who took him to his apartment where each masturbated the other. The patient was badly shaken by this experience and terrified of its implications, but nonetheless he conceded he was tremendously aroused sexually.

The patient was treated on the couch four times a week for 22 months for a total of 317 hours. The first six months of treatment were characterized by an amazing outpouring of diverse themes, of material that had been suppressed at the time of history giving, particularly of many anxiety-laden and chaotic sexual elements. There was no organizing theme or dominance of any single idea, but it was as though the first six months were a gargantuan catharsis for the patient. There were fantasies of submitting homosexually to male rivals; of submitting to a woman and becoming her slave; of becoming a woman; fears of castration from both men and women; fears of death; fears of abandonment and starvation; and numerous dreams of incestual desire and Oedipal rivalry. Interpretations were kept to a minimum during this period, not only because of the abundance of material, but also because there seemed to be no dominant motivational theme. The emphasis in treatment, therefore, was general. It was pointed out to him only that he seemed to view heterosexuality as threatening from a number of standpoints, i.e., fear of both the woman and the competing male. It should be noted that the chaos of his fantasy life was in marked contrast to his everyday life. He was a successful, hardworking student, somewhat constrained and obsessive in his behavior.

The therapist asumed that the patient, himself, sooner or later, when his fantasies impinged more closely on his real life, would begin to organize his thoughts and thus provide a more specific direction to the analysis. This was precisely what happened. A chance occurrence focused all of his attention on one aspect of his problems: his unresolved dependency needs. At the termination of the 90th session the patient accidentally caught sight of the therapist greeting his wife and children. This precipitated a series of reactions which deeply impressed the patient and led to his first real analytic insights. Up until then he had seen the therapist as a cold, ungiving, rigid man, very much like his father. When he saw the warmth of the therapist's greetings to his children, his own unfulfilled dependency came out full blast. He felt outraged and betrayed and stated that he did not want a "cold analytic approach" in treatment.

The patient then spent much time reevaluating his relationship with his father. He realized that as a child he saw his father as a huge, overpowering, dominating man, the acme of masculinity and strength. When the patient was 2½, the father accidentally dropped the boy from a height. The trauma was considered by the family physician to be the cause of a strabismus from which the patient suffered until it was corrected surgically when he was nine. This unfortunate incident markedly strengthened his unconscious belief that the father would castrate him in any competition, both Oedipal and non-Oedipal. He dealt with his hostility by repression and as much as possible he avoided competition in a tough, masculine world. Instead, he submitted to his father in an ingratiating way and sought, without much success, to remain dependent on him. In frustration, he turned more and more to the mother, who cooperated very nicely by being so overprotective. These essential dynamics of his dependency conflict emerged very clearly in a dream which expressed his sense of deprivation, earlier by the father, now by the therapist.

A man refused to serve him some meat. All that he gave him was tough gristle that was not good to eat. The patient, therefore, turned to a woman, who gave him nice, tender slices of beef.

The interpretation of his dependency transference generated depression, anxiety, and an upsurge of homosexual and pseudohomosexual fantasies. He became more overt in his demands for love and cure from the therapist and, simultaneously, more obsessively perfectionistic in his work. The latter was interpreted as a symbolic attempt to ingratiate himself with a parental authority figure. He reported numerous fantasies of fellatio upon the therapist, sometimes with erotic involvement, sometimes without. These were interpreted as a fusion of his sexual needs with his dependent desires. The threapist pointed out again and again how he withdrew from self-sufficiency and stewed instead in resentment at having to solve his own problems.

Gradually, the patient came out of his depression and his fantasy life quieted down. He was by this time an interne and began to be overtly competitive, iconoclastic, and hostile to superiors at the hospital. Episodes of competitive hostility were often followed by dreams of losing his masculinity in retaliation for his aggression. For example, after a bitter disagreement with a resident, he dreamed that he was examined before a group of doctors and exposed as having breasts. The emphasis in therapy began to fall on the penis as the instrument of power in competitive struggles with other men. The male figures in his dreams often appeared as hazy fusions of the therapist and his father. This trend culminated in two dreams; first, in which a middle-aged man accused him of raping a woman, and, second, in the dream that follows:

He was having intercourse with a woman. Just at the moment before ejaculation the door opened and there was his father. He jumped up terrified as though he had been caught doing something wrong.

With these dreams the patient finally grasped that he saw his father as the intimidating figure in his sexual desires for women, and the rivalry of the Oedipus complex for the first time became apparent to him. He also recognized that the true conflict felt in the therapy was with the father rather than with the therapist. These insights were followed by a group of castration dreams in which he saw himself as damaged, injured, or diseased in many different ways. It became clear that his cross-dressing masturbatory fantasies were a demonstration of submission to his father. Their purpose was to placate the father, ward off the castration threat, allay the castration anxiety, and thus permit the patient to carry the masturbation through to a pleasurable conclusion.

Spurred on by his new understanding, the patient embarked on a vigorous and active heterosexual existence with many different women. He did not engage in any sustained relationships, nor on his part was there very much emotional involvement; rather, he attempted through "acting out" to prove his masculinity. At no time did he have any mechanical difficulty in performance, in achieving or maintaining an erection, but he did complain at first of some diminution of pleasurable sensation in his penis. As time went on, though, his capacity for pleasure increased until after a few months he never complained of this anesthetic symptom again.

The sustained heterosexual activity set off a new trend in his analysis. Up to this point the therapy had dealt mainly with his relation to his father. The relation to the mother was not yet clarified. Now he began to have dreams in which he was having intercourse with older women. He became involved with a woman, who, though not older, was of a more mature nature and quite dominating in her attitudes. After a quarrel with her, he produced a typical "vagina dentata" dream:

He was in Africa. Two or three rhinoceroses ran out of the bush. A native woman dressed in a hula skirt said, "I'll show you how we catch these rhinos." He was surprised that she was not frightened that the beast would gore her. The woman got behind one of the animals, clamped her legs around him, and pulled him down on top of her. She grabbed him by the tail and that made him powerless. She had a little scissors. All of a sudden he was afraid she was going to cut the rhino's penis off. Then toward the end of the dream it became confused, and he felt it was his penis she was going to cut off.

This was the first of a number of similar dreams in which the emphasis was shifted from the competitive relationship with a man to the ideas of a dominant woman, who equally well could castrate him, either in the sexual act or in a nonsexual situation where he was forced to submit to her will. The prototype for this woman was, of course, his mother, who had dominated him through overprotection. She was the queenly woman to whom he submitted as a slave in his masturbatory fantasies.

With the analysis of this trend, his behavior with

women gradually altered and he began to form more meaningful relationships. In the final phase of therapy he fell in love, and after a prolonged courtship that lasted almost a year he married. Needless to say, until he made up his mind, all of the major themes that had been brought out before were reiterated. He remained in treatment for another five months, a period that was primarily observational to insure he could apply what he had learned. His marriage seemed to be working out well, his homosexual fantasies were almost nonexistent, and his sexual life seemed in every way normal. It was felt that he could manage alone, and therapy was terminated. The patient was seen five years later. He told the therapist that all his gains had been maintained. He was in the private practice of his specialty, he was very happy with his wife, and he was the father of two children.

Summary

We have described a psychodynamic formulation that we believe is useful in the psychotherapy of male homosexuality. It provides the therapist with an understanding of the unconscious motivations that impel the patient to flee from women and to seek contact with men. Such an understanding is essential to any therapy which makes use of insight to facilitate reversal of a homosexual pattern and the establishment of heterosexuality. We have shown how our formulation can be utilized in psychotherapy by presenting the clinical course of three successfully treated cases with follow-ups of five or more years. Our emphasis in this chapter has been on psychodynamics, rather than on technique, although we have indicated how a number of important technical maneuvers derive from an understanding of the psychodynamics.

Notes

CHAPTER 1:

1 Sigmund Freud: *Three Contributions to the Theory of Sex;* New York, N. and M. Disease Publishing Co., 1930. "Notes upon a Case of Obsessional Neurosis," *Collected Papers*, 3d. ed. 3:293–383; London, Hogarth Press, 1946. "Psycho-Analytic Notes upon an Autobiographical Account of a Case of Paranoia (Dementia Paranoides)," *Collected Papers* 3:387–470. "From the History of an Infantile Neurosis," *Collected Papers* 3:473–605. "The Psychogenesis of a Case of Homosexuality in a Woman," *Collected Papers* 2:202–231. "Certain Neurotic Mechanisms in Jealousy Paranoia and Homosexuality," *Collected Papers* 2:232–243. *New Introductory Lectures on Psycho-Analysis;* New York, Norton, 1933.

2 Sandor Rado, "A Critical Examination of the Concept of Bisexuality," *Psychosomatic Med.* (1940) 2:459–467.

3 Karen Horney, *The Neurotic Personality of Our Time;* New York, Norton, 1937.

4 Clara Thompson, "Changing Concepts of Homosexuality in Psychoanalysis," *Psychiatry* (1947) 10:183–189.

5 Sandor Rado, "An Adaptational View of Sexual Behavior," pp. 159–189; in *Psychosexual Development in Health and Disease*, edited by Paul H. Hoch and Joseph Zubin; New York, Grune and Stratton, 1949. Rado, unpublished lectures in psychodynamics, given at the Psychoanalytic Clinic for Training and Research, Columbia University, 1945–1953.

6 Abram Kardiner, *The Individual and His Society;* New York, Columbia University Press, 1945. Abram Kardiner and Lionel Ovesey, *The Mark of Oppression; A Psychosocial Study of the American Negro;* New York, Norton, 1951.

CHAPTER 2:

[1] See Sandor Rado, "Recent Advances of Psychoanalytic Therapy," chapter 5, section 2, in *Psychiatric Treatment* (prepared by the Association for Research in Nervous and Mental Diseases); Baltimore, Williams & Wilkins, 1953.

[2] See, for example, S. Zuckerman, *The Social Life of Monkeys and Apes;* London, Kegan, Paul, 1932.

[3] Sigmund Freud, "Psychoanalytic Notes upon an Autobiographical Account of a Case of Paranoia (Dementia Paranoides)," *Collected Papers*, 3d. ed. 3:387–470; London, Hogarth Press, 1946.

CHAPTER 3:

[1] Sigmund Freud, "Psychoanalytic Notes upon an Autobiographical Account of a Case of Paranoia (Dementia Paranoides)," *Collected Papers* 3:387–470; London, Hogarth Press, 1946.

[2] H. R. Klein and W. A. Horwitz, "Psychosexual Factors in the Paranoid Phenomena," *Amer. J. Psychiatry* (1949) 105: 697–701.

[3] *Ibid.*, p. 701.

[4] Freud, *op. cit.*, pp. 448–451.

[5] *Ibid.*, p. 445.

CHAPTER 4:

[1] This comparison has been made by several authors. See, for example, Clara Thompson, "The Role of Women in This Culture," *Psychiatry* (1941) 4:1–8. Viola Klein, *The Feminine Character;* New York, International Universities Press, 1948. Simone de Beauvoir, *The Second Sex;* New York, Knopf, 1953. For a discussion of the psychological effects of discrimination upon a minority group, see Abram Kardiner and Lionel Ovesey, *The Mark of Oppression: A Psychosocial Study of the American Negro;* New York, Norton, 1951.

[2] For an extensive discussion of dependency from an adapta-

tional point of view, see Abram Kardiner, *The Individual and His Society;* New York, Columbia University Press, 1939.

[3] See chapters 1, 2, and 3 of this volume.

[4] Sandor Rado, "Recent Advances in Psychoanalytic Therapy," pp. 42–58; in *Psychiatric Treatment* (prepared by the Association for Research in Nervous and Mental Disease); Baltimore, Williams and Wilkins, 1953. Lionel Ovesey and Jean Jameson, "The Adaptational Technique of Psychoanalytic Therapy," *Changing Concepts of Psychoanalysis;* New York, Grune and Stratton, 1956.

CHAPTER 5:

[1] A. Kardiner, A. Karush, and L. Ovesey, "A Methodological Study of Freudian Theory; I. Basic Concepts," *J. Nerv. Ment. Dis.* (1959) 129:11–19. Kardiner, Karush, and Ovesey, "A Methodological Study of Freudian Theory: II—The Libido Theory," *J. Nerv. Ment. Dis.* (1959) 129:133–143. Kardiner, Karush, and Ovesey, "A Methodological Study of Freudian Theory: III—Narcissism, Bisexuality, and the Dual Instinct Theory," *J. Nerv. Ment. Dis.* (1959) 129:207–221. Kardiner, Karush, and Ovesey, "A Methodological Study of Freudian Theory: IV—The Structural Hypothesis, The Problem of Anxiety, and Post-Freudian Ego Psychology," *J. Nerv. Ment. Dis.* (1959) 129:341–356.

[2] Chapters 1, 2, and 3 of this volume.

[3] S. Rado, "An Adaptational View of Sexual Behavior," pp. 186–213; in *Psychoanalysis of Behavior;* New York, Grune & Stratton, 1956.

[4] I. Bieber, et al., *Homosexuality, A Psychoanalytic Study of Male Homosexuals;* New York, Basic Books, 1962.

[5] A. Karush and L. Ovesey, "Unconscious Mechanisms of Magical Repair," *Arch. Gen. Psychiat.* (1961) 5:55–69.

[6] A. Maslow, H. Rand, and S. Neuman, "Some Parallels Between Sexual Dominance Behavior of Infra-Human Primates and the Fantasies of Patients in Psychotherapy," *J. Nerv. Ment. Dis.* (1960) 131:202–212.

[7] A. Karush, R. Easser, A. Cooper, and B. Swerdloff, "The Evaluation of Ego Strength: I—A Profile of Adaptive Balance," *J. Nerv. Ment. Dis.* (1965) 139:332.

Index

A

Adaptation, 19, 75–76
  homosexual, 21–22
  and masculine aspirations in
    women, 75–99
  and pseudohomosexual con-
    flict, 56–65
Adaptational analysis:
  of homosexual conflict, 15–
    31
  of masculine aspirations in
    women, 75–99
Aggression, 38–39
  inhibitions of, 57
Anal incorporation, 24, 64
Anal masturbation, 64
Anal rape, 40
Anxiety:
  castration, 18, 21, 23, 77–
    78, 88
  homosexual, and pseudoho-
    mosexual, 71
  pseudohomosexual, 32–51
Arousal, pleasurable, 114–115
Assertion, 38
  inhibitions of, 39, 56–67,
    61–65
Autoeroticism, 16–17

B

Behavior, and motivational
    goals, 28–30
Bisexuality:
  constitutional, 52
  Freud's concept of, 16–17
  Rado's concept of, 19
Breast, penis equated with, 22–
    24, 80, 82

C

Castration, symbolic, 86–87
Castration anxiety, 18, 21,
    77–78
Castration fantasy, 23
Children:
  aggression of, 57
  dependency of, 20–21
  sexual behavior of, 16–18

D

Delusions:
  of jealousy, 55
  of persecution, 54–55
Dependency:
  and breast-fantasy, 22–23
  as cannibalistic act, 92
  of children, 20–21
  definition of, 79–80
  motivation, 61–65, 79–84
Dreams:
  and dependency, 80–82
  and power motive, 58–61
  and pseudohomosexual anx-
    iety, 38–49

E

Ego strength, 109–112
Erotomania, 55

F

Fantasies:
  breast, 22
  castration, 23, 58
  reparative infantile, 24–28